GALILEO

The Man, his Work, his Misfortunes

296
maggio

1624

Galileo Galilei fiorentino

Portrait of Galileo by Ottavio Leoni.

GALILEO

The Man, his Work, his Misfortunes

James Brodrick S.J.

HARPER & ROW, PUBLISHERS
New York

© James Brodrick S.J., 1964

PRINTED IN GREAT BRITAIN FOR HARPER & ROW,
PUBLISHERS, INCORPORATED, NEW YORK

To

my dear friend

Jane, in Arizona

Contents

The Formation of a Genius   13

Struggles with the Aristotelians   29

A Crusader in Rome   55

Religion and Science   73

The First Brush with the Inquisition   101

The Wrangler   113

Eclipse   127

Brief Bibliography of Works in English   147

Index   149

Illustrations

Galileo in 1624   *Frontispiece*

1. The Ptolemaic universe   *facing page* 30
2. Ferdinand I de' Medici   31
3. Cosimo II de' Medici   40
4. Galileo's drawing of the moon   41
5. Galileo's house at Padua   56
6. Tycho Brahe's celestial globe   57
7. Procession of the Doge of Venice   64
8. Pope Paul V   65
9. Pope Urban VIII   96
10. Frontispiece of Il *Saggiatore*   128
11. Ferdinand II de' Medici   129
12. Convent of S. Maria Sopra Minerva, where Galileo made his public recantation   144
13. The pendulum clock   145

                             In text page

The Copernican system of the universe   36

Tycho Brahe's planetary system   37

Facsimile of Galileo's drawing of Saturn and its 'attendant stars'   48

The Formation
of a Genius

The Formation
of a Genius

THE city of Pisa has had a long and rich history. After Florence, whose river Arno it shares, it is the most enthralling place in Tuscany. In ancient Roman times it lay on the sea, but deposits of mud from the Arno have gradually pushed the Mediterranean six miles back. From the beginning of the eleventh century, Pisa rivalled Genoa and Venice as a centre of world trade. It took the lead in the struggle against Islam and defeated the Saracens not only in Italian waters but on their own home ground of Tunisia.

The valiant city was equally prominent in the general Crusades, and commemorated its victories, such as a ding-dong naval battle off Palermo in 1063, by the building of a magnificent cathedral, within which were placed sixty-eight ancient columns brought home by the Pisans from their campaigns. Besides the cathedral, in the Piazza del Duomo are three other works of supreme art, the Baptistery, the Campanile, better known as the Leaning Tower, and the Campo Santo, 'a group of buildings unique in their lovely and lonely majesty'.[1] For the Campo Santo fifty-three shiploads of earth were brought from Jerusalem, and it has not its match for beauty as a burial ground elsewhere on earth. Pisa and Genoa had long been contending for the lordship of the Mediterranean, but Genoa prevailed and decisively defeated her rival's fleet in the year 1284. Pisa, however, maintained her independence as a republic until 1406 when she fell under the yoke of Florence, and became part of the Medicean Grand Duchy of Tuscany in 1569.

Five years before that date, on February 15, 1564, Galileo Galilei was born in Pisa to a Florentine father, Vincenzo Galilei, a man of good family but of very modest means. He earned just enough as a cloth merchant in a small way to be able to send his son to school at the monastery of Vallombrosa where Galileo developed a vocation and joined the monastic novitiate. Vincenzo cherished less heavenly ambitions for his talented son and promptly brought him home to Florence to tutor him personally.

The impoverished vendor of cloth was a highly accomplished mathematician, musician and composer, in whose many books on musical theory can be seen traits later characteristic of his son, particularly a distrust of and contempt for arguments based on authority. From this pugnacious but devoted father Galileo acquired an excellent

[1] Baedeker's *Italy*, 1962.

knowledge of mathematics and his lifelong enthusiasm for music, with a particular addiction to the lute, of which he became a master. It was probably also from his father that he received lessons in drawing for which he showed a natural flair. He might indeed have become a considerable artist had he given his mind to it. Though his published verses are undistinguished, there dwelt in him the soul of a major poet, as many passages of his prose works attest. He was an exceedingly gifted man, and unfortunately he knew it. As a fervent modern admirer of his, the German Rudolf Thiel, says candidly: 'By nature this great scientist and scholar was bellicose, passionate, spiteful, ruthlessly determined and unscrupulous in his choice of methods.'

At twenty-three Galileo coveted the chair of mathematics at the university of Bologna but, despite a great deal of canvassing for the post, failed to obtain it. His father then persuaded him to switch over to medicine, which, in that age of ever-multiplying diseases, was the most lucrative of all professions. Vincenzo drew on his scanty resources to enrol his son as a student of medicine at the University of Pisa, then under the sway of Florence which had no university of its own. The great name in medicine at the time and for long afterwards was Claudius Galen who, though born in Asia Minor and educated at Alexandria, practised for most of his life in Rome where he became physician to Marcus Aurelius. Not only his vast knowledge of Greek medical history, to which he contributed 117 original treatises of his own, but his devoutly religious attitude to medicine ensured his popularity with both Christians and Moslems throughout the Middle Ages and subsequently.

15

William Harvey, who in 1628 made the great medical breakthrough of discovering the circulation of the blood, was educated on Galen's theories. But Galen was taught rather woodenly at Pisa and Galileo, never one to suffer boredom gladly, made himself a perfect nuisance in the lecture room by contesting his professor's statements and adducing counter-arguments to those propounded by Galen. He became known in university circles as the wrangler and showed such an antipathy to medicine that his father reluctantly permitted him to give it up. Luckily for him, there were people who admired his wit and originality. The Marchese Guido Ubaldo del Monte used his considerable influence to obtain for him the chair of mathematics at Pisa, which had fallen vacant. It was a wretchedly paid position, but gave him the satisfaction of working in his chosen field. He was then twenty-five.

Six years earlier, according to a romantic tale, possibly containing a few grains of truth, when he was contending with Galen, he had paid a visit of·devotion one day to the cathedral of Pisa, which boasts a very wonderfully sculptured bronze sanctuary lamp. It had been newly replenished with oil just before Galileo came in, and was swinging gently to rest. He had not gone far with his prayers when a sudden thought put an end to them altogether. The swings of the lamp, whether long or short, seemed to take the same time, which he proved in a rough and ready fashion by using his pulse beats as a chronometer. He had stumbled on the isochronism of the pendulum.

During his three years' professorship at Pisa, the young gadfly could not refrain from exasperating the more die-hard Aristotelians at the University. He certainly under-estimated the genius of Aristotle, which was greater even than his own. Building on the mathematical analysis of planetary motion worked out a few years earlier by his contemporaries Eudoxus and Callippus, Aristotle con-structed a physical system of the heavens which was very largely original. He postulated a stationary earth, the region of change, of generation and decay, with its corruptible ele-ments of earth, water, air and fire. Beyond this dust-bin of the universe lay the moon, the planets and the fixed stars, all composed of a fifth element, a quintessence which rendered them immune from any change except motion in circles round the earth. The circles had come to be con-ceived as vast, hollow, solid but invisible crystalline spheres, carrying in the rims the Moon, Mercury, Venus, the Sun, Mars, Jupiter, Saturn and the fixed stars. Using first-class mathematical analysis, Aristotle found that fifty-five such spheres were required in order to give a physical and mathematical explanation of the apparent irregularity of the planetary paths, which he conceived to be com-pounded of four or five different circular motions. Though wrong in fact, as Galileo was so startlingly to prove, this theory did provide plausible physical explanations of a wide range of celestial phenomena.

Wise after the event, and with his telescope to assist, Galileo did not give Aristotle sufficient credit as a great pioneering astronomer, with nothing but his mathematics and his brilliant mind to help him.

Aristotle's theories were given further elaboration and improvement by two geniuses of the first rank, the Greek Hipparchus who flourished at Rhodes during the second century B.C., and the Egyptian Claudius Ptolemy who became illustrious at Alexandria during the second century A.D. Ptolemy's astronomical treatise, known by its Arabic title as the *Almagest*, is a complete exposition of the views and theories of Hipparchus, with improvements and extensions of detail by Ptolemy himself. From the information provided in the *Almagest* Hipparchus has come to be regarded by historians of the science as one of the greatest astronomers of all time. Ptolemy resurrected the ingenious Greek theory of epicycles and eccentrics to account for the non-circular motion of the planets, particularly Mars. The *Almagest* so effectively 'saved the appearances' of the heavens, helped navigation, and enabled eclipses to be predicted, that it became the astronomical bible of the Western world for fourteen centuries, until the Pole, Canon Nicholas Copernicus, provided an alternative and much simpler explanation of the heavenly phenomena by postulating the movement of the earth around the sun in his great, largely mathematical treatise, *On the Revolutions of the Celestial Orbs* (*De Revolutionibus Orbium Coelestium*), published in 1543, with a dedication to Pope Paul III.

Owing to the magnificent synthesis of Christian doctrine which St Thomas Aquinas had constructed on the basis of Aristotle's metaphysical and other writings, the Stagyrite, as he was called from the place of his birth in Greece, gradually assumed an extraordinary dominance over the minds of men in every sphere of intellectual inquiry, and particularly in what would now be called the field of natural science. Aristotle had been pre-eminent in this field, and his work on zoology, for instance, deeply impressed even such a master as Charles Darwin.

As a pioneer the great man inevitably made mistakes. By the sixteenth century, a highly authoritarian age, even his mistakes had become sacred dogmas which to question was considered impious. Aristotle himself would have been the first to scorn such an attitude, but there it was, and Galileo, who had so much in common with the splendid investigator of antiquity, reacted against it with all the vigour and violence at his command, thus doing true science an enormous service.

One cherished dogma of the Aristotelians was that the acceleration of falling bodies depended on their weights. A heavier body was presumed to fall faster than a lighter one. Galileo divined that in a vacuum, which he had not the means of creating, all bodies accelerated in falling at an equal rate. There is a tradition that he climbed the 294 steps to the platform of the leaning tower of Pisa and dropped a cannon ball and a bullet. To his delight they reached the ground at almost the same time. But this, like the pendulum story, is probably only a romantic tale.

Our gadfly at Pisa earned the dislike and hostility not only of his colleagues but of an illegitimate son of the Grand Duke, who had invented a machine for dredging the harbour of Leghorn. Galileo, already well known for his gifts as a mechanic, was asked to inspect the contraption and bluntly condemned it as useless for its purpose.

The general enmity which he had provoked determined him in 1592 to move out of the jurisdiction of Florence altogether. Once again, his good friend the Marchese Guido Ubaldo del Monte, who himself possessed great scientific talent, used his influence to secure for him the long-vacant chair of mathematics at the university of Padua in the Republic of Venice. Galileo remained at Padua for no less than eighteen years and there accomplished most of the work in mechanics which lies at the basis of modern physics, though he did not publish his results until long afterwards. His bent was to practical mathematics, that is, the application of mathematical concepts to observed phenomena—'something that has never had much appeal to pure mathematicians'.[1]

In 1594 Galileo, who was careless of his health while in eager pursuit of some new truth in nature, suffered a severe chill that resulted in a permanent arthritic condition. About four years later he took as mistress a handsome Venetian girl named Marina Gamba who remained steadfastly faithful to him until, after many years, he chose to end the union. In the year 1600 there was born to him of this liaison a daughter who was christened Virginia. Another daughter, Livia, was born the following year, and in 1606 a son, named Vincenzo after his grandfather. These children seem to have been an embarrassment to their father, busy with his lectures and mechanical inventions, and the care of them devolved upon their unmarried mother who proved worthy

[1] Stillman Drake, *Discoveries and Opinions of Galileo*, New York, 1957, p. 15.

of the trust. When in 1610 Galileo abandoned Padua after eighteen years residence in the Venetian Republic, he did not think it would help his worldly prospects to bring his mistress with him to his native Tuscany. But he had a scruple about the children and reluctantly took them along. Marina Gamba accepted her dismissal serenely and married in 1613 Giovanni Bartoluzzi, a Venetian. Galileo continued to finance the lady up to her marriage and kept in friendly correspondence with the couple who, for their part, took a keen interest in the three children. Vincenzo remained with his mother in Padua until her marriage and then became Galileo's responsibility.

From the way he treated them, especially the two girls, he did not deserve in the least that they should afterwards in evil times prove the greatest comfort of his existence. He decided to hide them away from the world and obtained from his friend, Cardinal Bandini, a faculty entitling them to take vows as nuns in the Convent of San Matteo at Arcetri, a short distance from Florence, as soon as they reached the canonical age of sixteen. Their ages at the time of entrance were Virginia thirteen and Livia twelve, innocent little victims of scientific discovery. It was a poor convent and the children were half-starved. Livia collapsed under her privations and sorrows, but her sister, in religion Suor Maria Celeste, rose magnificently above the tragic conditions, 'with the sublime purity and sweet tenderness of a loving woman's heart who had come to understand sorrow in her own experience, and the misery and errors of [her father] only to feel compassion for them and to alleviate their consequences'.[1] The boy Vincenzo was legitimized by Galileo's former pupil, Cosimo II, who succeeded to the ducal throne of Tuscany in 1609. He turned out well, and like his sister Maria Celeste, became a great comfort to his negligent father in the years of adversity.

Galileo's own father died in the summer of 1591 which meant that he, as the eldest son, had become responsible for his dour and somewhat scarifying mother, Giulia, his brother Michelangelo, just started on a musical career, and his sisters Elena and Livia, while their elder sister Virginia, married to Benedetto Landucci, had yet to receive her dowry. To meet all these obligations the unfortunate professor of mathematics at Pisa had a salary of sixty crowns a year. He had tried his best to win some recognition among learned men by giving private lectures in Florence and Siena on such subjects as 'Hell according to Dante's structure of it', 'Notes on the poetry of Ariosto', and 'Considerations on Tasso'. A university ordinance requiring professors to wear the traditional gown drew from him an ironic poem, *Contro il portar la toga.*

It was the feeling that he could never improve his prospects in Tuscany, as well as his unpopularity there, which caused Galileo to cast a covetous eye on the vacant mathematical chair at the University of Padua, in the Republic of Venice. His friend the Marchese promised to do everything in his power and drew his distinguished brother, Cardinal del Monte, into the battle for the chair.

[1] A. Banfi, *Vita di Galileo Galilei,* Paperback Edition, Milan, 1962, pp. 101-2. Antonio Banfi, who died in 1957, sat in the Italian Senate as a Communist deputy. There is hardly a trace of his Marxism in this admirable life of Galileo, first published in 1930.

They prevailed with the Venetian Council who issued a decree appointing Galileo chief professor of mathematics at the University of Padua at a salary of 180 florins a year. It was not a great improvement on his Tuscan salary, but the Paduan post offered prospects beyond any he could have hoped for in Tuscany.

The Del Montes gave their young protégé of thirty-two an introduction to one of the great men of Padua—Giovanni Vincenzo Pinelli, whose palazzo near Il Santo, as the many domed basilica of St Anthony is called, was the resort of all the distinguished residents or visitors known to the university. Pinelli had come into the world in Naples, born of a wealthy Genoese family. The product of a fine education, he spoke several languages and was an esteemed classical scholar. He delighted to help and encourage bright young men such as Galileo who would have met at his home eminent personages of the quality of Paolo Sarpi, the Servite Friar from Venice, Councillor of the Republic. Sarpi took a strong liking to Galileo and the two men became excellent friends.

Even more fruitful and satisfying was the friendship of the Venetian gentleman Giovanni Francesco Sagredo, whom Galileo was to immortalize. Sagredo, a very eminent mathematician, was drawn towards the Tuscan by an affinity of character, both being strongly religious and at the same time genial and sociable men. Through Sagredo's good offices Galileo's salary was increased from 180 florins to 320, little enough considering that he had to provide for two families. He paid for his sister Livia's education in a convent, and when, in 1601, she became engaged to Taddeo

Galletti, he guaranteed to pay that gentleman a dowry of eighteen hundred ducats, which he borrowed from his bank. He atoned for his bad treatment of his own children by almost beggaring himself to support his mother and his brothers and sisters. Michelangelo, his musical brother, was a ne'er-do-well and a heavy burden on his patience and his pocket for a long period.

As at Pisa, he fell back on private lessons to augment his income, and even opened an academy to spite bad fortune. It was situated close to Il Santo and roomy enough to lodge twenty guests whom he dined and wined with the most lavish generosity. With all his faults, and he has plenty, it is impossible not to like him.

In 1597 Galileo, always thinking of new ways in which to turn an honest penny, devised a great improvement to a mathematical instrument already in use. He called his revised version the 'geometric and military compass'. It would have proved invaluable to engineers, enabling them to solve expeditiously a wide variety of problems and calculations in this period just before Napier invented logarithms. In Padua, the new compass became quickly known and demand for it sufficiently lively to justify the inventor in employing a craftsman to produce it in quantities for sale.

Four years later, 1601, Galileo applied to the reigning family at Florence, the Medici, for appointment as tutor in mathematics to the heir apparent Cosimo II, when he had grown old enough to benefit. This came about in 1605 and the applicant, whose gifts had evidently not been forgotten, secured the post. Of course, he could only do his tutoring, which included instruction in the use of his improved compass, when the university of Padua was in its summer recess. After his opening session with his boy pupil Cosimo, he returned to the university to prepare his first book, a dry handbook for the guidance of buyers of the compass. This he published at his own house in 1606, with a dedication to his princely pupil in honour of whom he wrote it in Tuscan, that is to say, Italian. Hardly had the handbook appeared when a similar work in Latin followed, written by a young student whom Galileo esteemed and had actually taught the use of the new compass. It was a graceless and brazen thing to do, a piece of outrageous plagiarism which Galileo determined to annihilate. He brought an action against the culprit, Baldassare Capra, in the university courts, and had no less a person than Paolo Sarpi for his counsel. He won hands down and the wretched Capra had to appear at the sound of a trumpet to hear sentence pronounced against him at the time when there was the greatest assembly of students. The Latin lucubration was confiscated and burnt but Galileo, fearing that a few copies might escape to damage his reputation, published at Venice, in 1607, a devastating *Defence against the Calumnies and Impostures of Baldassar Capra*. Capra, 'a venom-spitting basilisque', must have wished on reading it that he had never been born.

Apart from that little foray into polemics, a foretaste of fireworks to come, Galileo was not well or widely known at the age of forty-five, with more than half his life behind him. At the beginning of the year 1609 he had been seventeen years in the gracious city of St Anthony, with a reputation for good teaching but with no printed work to his name except the little technical pamphlet about his compass. A year later his name was a household word all over Europe and he had qualified for the company of the immortals.

Struggles with the
Aristotelians

Struggles with the Aristotelians

THE astonishing change in Galileo's fortunes, which might also have been said to change the fortunes of the human race, was brought about by a small Latin pamphlet published under the title of *The Starry Messenger*—*Sidereus Nuncius*—at Venice in March, 1610. The full title of this epoch-making pamphlet was: *The Starry Messenger*, revealing great, unusual and remarkable spectacles, opening these to the consideration of every man, and especially of philosophers and astronomers; as observed by Galileo Galilei, Gentleman of Florence, Professor of Mathematics in the University of Padua, with the aid of a spyglass *lately invented by him*, in the surface of the moon, in innumerable Fixed Stars, in Nebulae, and above all in four planets swiftly revolving about Jupiter at differing distances and periods, and known to no one before the Author recently perceived them and decided that they should be named the Medicean Stars.

The whole tremendous story started with a rumour which reached Galileo from Flanders to the effect that a certain grinder of lenses for spectacles named Hans Lipperhey had chanced upon a property of combined concave and convex lenses, that of making distant objects seem nearer. Lipperhey actually constructed a primitive type of telescope and put it on the market. A friend of Galileo in Paris had seen a specimen of the new toy, for that is all it was, and told him what it looked like, whereupon he set to work with feverish energy to make such an instrument himself. He tells us how he proceeded:

> First I prepared a tube of lead at the end of which I fitted two glass lenses, both plane on one side, while on the other side, one was spherically convex and the other concave. Then placing my eye near the concave lens I perceived objects ... three times closer and nine times larger than when seen by the naked eye alone. Next, I constructed another one, more accurate, which represented objects as enlarged more than sixty times. Finally, sparing neither labour nor expense, I succeeded in constructing for myself so excellent an instrument that objects seen by it appeared nearly one thousand times larger and over thirty times closer than when regarded with our actual vision.[1]

As Banfi puts it, by Galileo's genius the *cannocchiale* was elevated 'from being a mere optical curiosity into a most efficient instrument for the acquisition of knowledge'.

In August, 1609, Galileo took his finest *cannocchiale* or

[1] *The Starry Messenger*, Stillman Drake's translation in *Discoveries and Opinions of Galileo*, p. 29.

1. The Ptolemaic universe, showing the earth at the centre surrounded by the elements of water, air (in the form of clouds) and fire. From G. Reisch, *Margarita Philosophiae*, Heidelberg, 1504.

2. Ferdinand I de' Medici, 1549–1609. *From a painting by Bronzino.*

spyglass, which was not named a telescope until some time later, with him to Venice. There he invited friends to come with him to the top of the campanile of St Mark's and examine the city and the countryside through his spyglass. So great was the astonishment and enthusiasm created by the experience that Galileo thought he ought to present the spyglass gratis to the ruling authorities, at the same time explaining how valuable it would be in time of war: 'We could discover the enemy's ships more than two hours sooner than he could discover us.' The Doge and his Council expressed their appreciation the following day by confirming Galileo in his post for life and increasing his salary to the extraordinary sum of a thousand florins a year.

So great a reward caused envious tongues to wag. Some said that a Frenchman had sold an instrument exactly resembling Galileo's there in Venice for four or five lire. Before that eventful year 1609 was out Galileo would show his detractors whether he had tricked the Serene Republic into paying him such an extravagant salary. He had many excellent reasons for wanting all the money he could legitimately get, but money was far from being his first consideration, as would appear the following year.

Towards the end of the year 1609 Galileo turned his telescope, to give the instrument the name it would soon bear, on the Paduan night sky where rode a crescent moon. This he carefully observed night after chilly night while it waxed to fullness, and found that besides the large spots visible to the naked eye, fancifully called the man in the moon, there are other spots smaller in size all over the lunar

31

surface which 'have never been seen by anybody before me'. From repeated observations of these smaller spots he was led to the conviction 'that the surface of the moon is not smooth, uniform and precisely spherical, as a great number of philosophers believe it (and the other heavenly bodies) to be, but is uneven, rough and full of cavities and prominences, being not unlike the face of the earth, relieved by chains of mountains and deep valleys'. He estimated the height of some lunar mountains to be four miles, which is very close to the calculations of more recent astronomers. He explains how he arrives at his conclusions and promises that in a book he has planned to write called *The System of the World*, he will prove by an infinitude of arguments that 'the earth is a wandering body surpassing the moon in splendour, and not the sink of all dull refuse of the universe', as Aristotle and his followers through the ages declared it to be.

By his observations of the moon Galileo utterly discredited the age-old theory that the heavenly bodies, beginning with the moon, were composed of an aether or quintessence, a fifth ultimate substance, unchangeable and incorruptible, in contrast to the four sublunary elements, air, fire, water and earth which are subject to constant mutation and decay. Our globe, the outcast and pariah of the heavens, was restored at a stroke to the comity of the stars.

Galileo, at once iconoclast and matchless observer, then turned his telescope on those same fixed stars. In *The Starry Messenger* he supplied diagrams of those in two constellations, Orion and the Pleiades, 'in order to give one or two proofs of their almost inconceivable number'. Confining

32

himself to the belt and sword of Orion, in addition to the nine stars known from remote antiquity, he found eighty adjacent stars never before seen by human eyes. The Pleiades, instead of being a cosy little family of seven sisters, proved to be a tribe of forty stars. Better telescopes than Galileo's have sent the number in the group up to five hundred. But in all conscience Galileo's instrument made astounding revelations, for instance, that the Milky Way is 'nothing but a congeries of innumerable stars grouped together in clusters . . . many of them rather large and quite bright, while the number of small ones is altogether beyond calculation'. These were enthralling discoveries, but the best was yet to be. One can feel Galileo's excitement when he comes to relate what happened, 'the seventh day of January in this year 1610 at the first hour of night'.

Galileo had studied the planet Jupiter a little earlier without noticing anything out of the ordinary. That night of January 7 he was using his finest telescope and observed that beside the planet were three small, very bright, stars, two to the east of Jupiter and one to the west. He says: 'They aroused my curiosity somewhat by appearing to lie in an exact straight line parallel to the ecliptic'. But he did not give them much attention, assuming them to form part of the great host of fixed stars. Every night he was discovering hundreds of fixed stars never seen before and, as the pre-eminent Galilean authority, Mr Stillman Drake, has remarked, it shows his genius as an observer that he had noticed and remembered those three simply by reason of their alignment and recalling them so well that when by chance he happened to see them the following night, he was certain they had changed their position, all three being in a straight line to the west of Jupiter, closer together, and at equal intervals from one another.

Galileo's curiosity was now thoroughly aroused. What in the name of Canon Copernicus was going on in the heavens where Jupiter reigned? The very puzzled observer, no doubt shivering from the cold, began to wonder whether the computations of all earlier astronomers that Jupiter was at this time, according to the appearances, journeying westward among the fixed stars were not erroneous. What if it were moving eastwards and had overtaken the three stars he had seen? The next night, January 9, might provide a clue to the mystery, so he awaited it impatiently. But the sky was completely overcast. To his deep content the night of January 10 was clear and he took up his chilly post with eagerness, in attendance on the Lord Jupiter. This time only two of the mysterious stars showed themselves, both east of the planet. He wrote:

As at first, they were in the same straight line with Jupiter, and were arranged precisely in the line of the zodiac. Noticing this, and knowing that there was no way in which such alterations could be attributed to Jupiter's motion, yet being certain that these were still the same stars I had observed (in fact no other was to be found along the line of the zodiac for a long way on either side of Jupiter), my perplexity was now transformed into amazement. I was sure that the apparent changes belonged not to Jupiter but to the observed stars, and I resolved to pursue this investigation with greater care and attention.[1]

[1] *The Starry Messenger,* translation from Stillman Drake, *Discoveries and Opinions of Galileo,* p. 52.

Night after freezing night, the dedicated, indomitable observer watched the starlets as they did their dance around Jupiter. On January 13 he found yet another member of Jupiter's family, making them four, one to the east and three in a humped shape to the west.

Sometimes he appears to have stayed up half the night, 'for the revolutions of these planets are so speedily completed that it is usually possible to take even their hourly variations'. On February 26 he wanted to observe the progress of Jupiter and his attendant quartette along the line of the zodiac in relation to some convenient fixed star. All his observations for the four days following were made in relation to this fixed star. He stopped observing on March 2 and had his pamphlet announcing and describing his discoveries in print by the end of the month. As he wished to attract the attention of learned men all over Europe, he wrote in Latin and supplied admirable drawings of the moon, as well as diagrams of the stars in various nebulae and of Jupiter's moons in all their variety. No other planetary moon except the earth's had been discovered at that time, and some men who were disposed to accept the Copernican system had their faith in it disturbed by the earth's privilege. Now, wrote Galileo triumphantly:

We have not just one planet rotating about another while both run through a great orbit around the sun; our own eyes show us four stars which wander around Jupiter, as the moon does around the earth, while all together trace out a grand revolution about the sun in the space of twelve years.[1]

[1] The eminent publicist Arthur Koestler, who was himself trained as a scientist, is extremely critical of Galileo's pretensions. He object

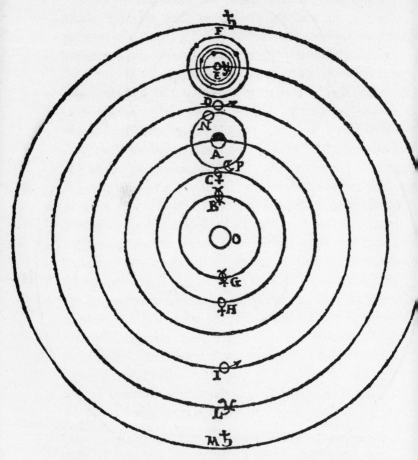

The Copernican system of the universe, reprinted from Galileo's Dialogue. It shows the planets marked by astrological signs revolving round the sun.

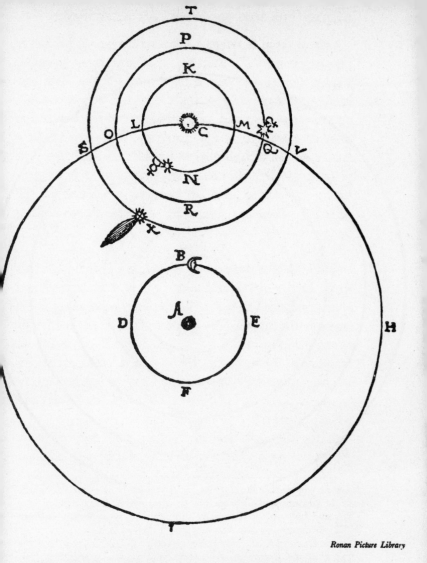

Tycho Brahe's planetary system, reprinted from De Mundi aetherei recentioribus Phaenomenis, 1577.

One of those to whom Galileo sent copies of his *Starry Messenger* was the imperial mathematician, Johannes Kepler. Galileo had first entered into relations with this engaging if wayward genius thirteen years before, in 1597, and they had remained good friends ever since. Kepler was so much enthralled by *The Starry Messenger* that he had a second edition of it printed at Frankfurt in 1610, the year of its original publication. Five years later a Jesuit missionary in Peking gave an account in Chinese of the principal discoveries revealed in the epoch-making pamphlet.

While Galileo was nightly probing the Paduan skies, his friend Kepler in Prague had brought to a triumphant end a long and gruelling war with the planet Mars, using as his weapons the marvellously accurate data on the behaviour of the planet provided by the great Danish observational astronomer, Tycho Brahe. Tycho died in 1601 and Kepler was then appointed to the vacant post of mathematician to the Emperor Rudolf II, soon to resign his throne and become demented.

In the enormous and momentous tome called *A New Astronomy or a Physics of the Sky*, Kepler tells at great

---

that he was neither the first nor the only scientist to point a telescope at the heavens and discover new wonders there. Thomas Harriot in England had studied the moon through a telescope before Galileo. Koestler maintains also that Galileo's drawings and diagrams in the *Starry Messenger* are extremely defective. But he admits that the impact of the pamphlet, its cumulative effect, was tremendous, 'like a punch in the solar plexus on those grown up in the traditional view of the bounded universe' (*The Sleepwalkers. A History of Man's Changing Vision of the Universe*, London, 1959, pp. 366-7.)

length and in obscure Latin of all the wrong leads and blind alleys into which he had blundered in his fight against Mars, 'who made a great mockery of all the stratagems of astronomers, wrecked their tools, defeated their hosts'. At long last, though, the planet had met his match, for Kepler by the most extraordinary process of trial and error discovered the source of confusion in all earlier theories of planetary motion. It was that Mars does not pursue its journey around the sun in a circular orbit as Plato had decreed and all subsequent students of the heavens until Kepler had devoutly believed. It moves in an orbit that this great man eventually discovered to be an ellipse with the sun in one focus. This discovery, come by with so much heart-break and frustration, cleared the skies for ever of epicycles and other such imaginary machinery. The *New Astronomy* contained also two of Kepler's three famous laws which enabled Isaac Newton to establish his theory of gravitation. Arthur Koestler gives a thrilling account of the steps by which Kepler reached his conclusions, and shows in the process the amount of chance and sheer luck which attend on scientific discovery.[1] Kepler, though a devout Lutheran, was also a devout Copernican, in spite of the opposition of Luther and Melanchthon to heliocentrism on scriptural grounds. Tycho Brahe objected to the Copernican theory more for physical-mechanical than religious reasons and devised a cosmic system of his own in which the five known planets travelled round the sun, and the sun with the planets in tow orbited the earth. This compromise theory answered satisfactorily a great

[1] *The Sleepwalkers*, op. cit., pp. 313-43.

number of astronomical problems, and so could be regarded as a stage towards full Copernicanism, if that should ever be proved beyond all cavil. Among the many who rallied to Tycho's theory were the Jesuit astronomers in Rome who, though they at first greatly admired Galileo, did not consider that his discoveries proved the earth to be in motion round the sun.[1]

Reactions to *The Starry Messenger* were amusing and astonishing in their extent and variety. A few weeks before France's great king, Henri Quatre, was assassinated by Ravaillac, Galileo received a letter from a French diplomat to the following effect:

> The second request, but the most urgent one that I have to make is that you would decide, should you discover any other

[1] While obviously and rightly loving Kepler with all his foibles, Mr. Koestler shows himself very harsh to Galileo, who certainly took the initiative in opening correspondence with Kepler in 1597. He was thirty-three at the time, seven years older than the German astronomer, to whom he confessed that he had long held the Copernican theory of the universe and had written many arguments in support of it, but was deterred from publishing them from fear of drawing on his head, as Copernicus himself had done, the ridicule and derision of an infinite number of fools, meaning the dyed-in-the-wool Aristotelians. Kepler had never heard of Galileo, and his recently published *Podromus* came into Galileo's hands quite accidentally and inspired his letter to its author. He told Kepler that he would comment on the book in due course but never did so. His failure has been construed by Mr Koestler as churlish. It was not. On the contrary, as Mr Stillman Drake has pointed out, it was an act of charity. 'Having read beyond the Preface, Galileo could only have found himself in a sea of Pythagorean speculations of the sort most distasteful to him; the Kepler of 1596 and the *Podromus* was by no means the Kepler of 1609 and the *Astronomia Nova*.' (Stillman Drake, 'Origin and Fate of Galileo's Theory of the Tides', extracted from *Physis,* a Review of the history of science, vol. III—Fasc. 3—1961, p. 186, n. 2).

3. Cosmio II de' Medici, 1590–1621. *From a painting by Giusto Sustermans.*

4. A facsimile of Galileo's drawing of the moon from *Sidereus Nuncius*, 1610.

fine star, to call it by the name of the great star of France and the most brilliant of all stars; and, if it seems fitting to you, to call the star by his proper name of Henri rather than by his family name of Bourbon; thus you will have an opportunity of doing a thing just and due and proper in itself, and at the same time will render yourself and your family rich and powerful forever.

As against that flattering request, a worthy named Christmann wrote in an appendix to a Latin book entitled *The Gordian Knot*:

We are not to think that Jupiter has four satellites given him by nature in order, by revolving round him, to immortalize the name of Medici. These are the dreams of idle men, who love ludicrous ideas better than our laborious and industrious correction of the heavens. Nature abhors so horrible a chaos and to the truly wise such vanity is detestable.

Galileo himself was only too painfully aware of the Aristotelian opposition. Writing to a new friend who became possibly the dearest of his disciples, Benedetto Castelli, a brilliant young Benedictine monk, he said that for some people 'not even the testimony of the stars would suffice were they to descend on earth to speak for themselves'. Strangely, among his most obstinate opponents was one of his many personal friends, Cesare Cremonini, the chief professor of philosophy at Padua, considered by the Venetian Senate to be the principal ornament of their university. They showed their appreciation of him by conferring a stipend of two thousand florins, higher than that of any other professor.

41

The regard in which this man was held casts a good deal of light on the religious temperament of the Venetians. He taught the strictest Aristotelianism, as interpreted by the medieval Islamic philosopher Averroes (1126-98), whose views St Thomas Aquinas combated as destructive of Christianity. Those views were championed in Aquinas's own time by a group at the University of Paris headed by Siger de Brabant (c. 1235-82). Averroes 'had interpreted the rather obscure statements in the third book of Aristotle's *De Anima* as meaning that there is one immortal intellect which enters into temporary union with, or performs a function in, individual men. There is therefore no personal immortality ... we might speak, then, of the human race being in some sense immortal and of individuals as sharing in some sense in an impersonal immortality; but there would be no question of John or of Peter surviving death as recognizable individuals'.[1] For teaching that kind of thing Cremonini was paid twice as much as Galileo or any other professor and was given a palazzo as grand as a Roman cardinal's. Thought was certainly free in the Venetian Republic. Though on terms of friendship with Galileo, Cremonini would have nothing to do with his experiments or astronomical discoveries, for they touched on the honour of Aristotle. He admitted that he had not tried to see any of the discoveries, and added, 'I am of the opinion that nobody but Galileo has seen them. To look through that spyglass of his throws my head into confusion. Basta! I don't want to know anything more on the subject.'

[1] F. C. Copleston, *Aquinas*, Pelican Book A349, p. 171.

The Inquisition twice tried to arraign Cremonini for his Averroist heterodoxy, but the state intervened and stopped the process. For other reasons, Pope Paul V, a bureaucratic canonist with his head in the Middle Ages, put the government and city of Venice under an interdict in May, 1606, by the terms of which Mass might no longer be said nor the sacraments administered. The Doge and Council of Ten, who were not notorious for piety, ordered all priests in the city to say Mass daily and give the sacraments as usual. Paolo Sarpi became the hero of the hour and used his clever pen with tireless enthusiasm in defence of the Republic's stand. The Theatines, the Capuchins and the Jesuits were banished from Venice and Galileo, on a visit to the city, witnessed their departure on May 11, the day the interdict came into force. He described the scene to his brother, the musical Michelangelo:

> At two o'clock last night, the Jesuit Fathers were placed on board two ships to be transported beyond the confines of the State. They walked to the ship, each with a crucifix hanging round his neck and a lighted candle in his hand. Yesterday, after dinner, they were locked up in their house and two policemen were put on guard at the door to prevent anybody from entering or leaving the convent. I believe they are also to be expelled from Padua and the rest of the Venetian dominions, to the great regret and sorrow of many women who are devoted to them.

The 'molte donne loro devote' of this letter has a touch of Sarpi's sarcasm in it. As for the lighted candles, they may have been necessary in the small hours of the morning, if there was no moon. The unwise pope of the interdict was later on to engineer the first very unwise movement against Galileo.

Meantime, that worthy was on top of the world and busily scheming to secure an honourable position at the court of his pupil Cosimo II, who succeeded to the ducal throne of Tuscany in 1609. Cosimo himself, though he liked and esteemed Galileo, was made cautious by the older heads of his court and by the continued vicious and sarcastic criticism of *The Starry Messenger* on the part of the Aristotelians of both Venice and Tuscany. Magini, the man who had beaten Galileo in the contest for the chair of mathematics at Bologna, had become definitely jealous of him, and ridiculed in letters to eminent correspondents at home and abroad the 'pretended discovery of four planets'.

A young Lutheran disciple of this Magini named Horky wrote and published a fiery and libellous attack on Galileo which earned him a stinging rebuke from Kepler. Kepler, though he had no telescope to verify the discoveries listed in *The Starry Messenger*, had rallied to Galileo's defence from the first and had even published a *Dissertatio cum Nuncio Sidereo* telling why he placed implicit trust in the word of his Paduan friend. Galileo urged this witness of the imperial mathematician on Belisario Vinta, the secretary of state of Cosimo II. He had sent that prince, his natural sovereign, a fine telescope and told Vinta that His Highness 'need observe the Planet Jupiter for only three nights to satisfy himself of the truth of the moons, not for five months as I continually watched it until not the slightest shadow of doubt remained in my mind'.

During the Easter vacation of 1610 Galileo visited Pisa and there discussed his hopes and wishes with Vinta. He followed up this appeal with a long letter from Padua to the same man, giving many reasons why the Grand Duke could be quite certain that the Medicean planets named after him were there in the sky. Then he lays his cards on the table and tells how well placed he is in Padua, with a fine salary and hosts of friends and students:

> But because giving private lessons and taking scholars as boarders constitute something of an obstacle to me and impede my studies, I should like to live completely free from the one and largely free of the other. Hence if I am to return to my native land, I desire that the primary intention of His Highness shall be to give me leave and leisure to draw my works to a conclusion without my being occupied in teaching. . . . I should like my books (dedicated always to my Lord) to become my source of income, to say nothing of such inventions as no other prince can match. . . . The works which I must bring to conclusion are these. Two books on the system and constitution of the universe—an immense conception full of philosophy, astronomy, and geometry. Three books on local motion—an entirely new science in which no one else, ancient or modern, has discovered any of the most remarkable laws which I demonstrate to exist in both natural and violent movement; hence I may call this a new science and one discovered by me from its very foundations. Three books on mechanics, . . . and though other men have written on this subject what has been done is not one-quarter of what I write, either in quantity or otherwise. . . .

Galileo plainly did not suffer from excessive modesty, but geniuses rarely do, and he was a superlative genius. At the close of his long letter he said, if given the post by the Grand

Duke he would like to have the title of philosopher added to that of mathematician. In July, 1610, four months after the publication of *The Starry Messenger*, he was granted his heart's desire and appointed chief mathematician and philosopher to the Grand Duke of Tuscany, at an annual salary of one thousand florins. At the same time he was made head mathematician of the University of Pisa, without obligation to reside or teach there.[1]

The Doge and Senate of the Venetian republic were extremely angry about the departure of their first mathematician, and regarded Galileo's action as a show of black ingratitude. But it has to be said for him that he could never have attained the leisure for experimenting and writing which he so richly deserved from a republic, however splendid and generous. As he put it: 'So long as I am capable of lecturing and serving, no one in the republic can exempt me from duty while I receive pay. In brief, I can hope to enjoy these benefits only from an absolute ruler.' His closest friend and best adviser on practical affairs at Venice, Sagredo, was absent on a diplomatic mission when Galileo left for Tuscany. On his return to Venice a year later this devoted man addressed a moving and eloquent letter to the vanished mathematician. He told of the many cities he had seen in his travels and compares them with his beloved Venice: 'Truly it seems to me that

---

[1] Stillman Drake, *Discoveries and Opinions of Galileo*, pp. 60-5. Mr Drake suggests that the decisive reason for Galileo's return to Tuscany was nostalgia. 'He was a Florentine by lineage and early training, living abroad among Venetians. The differences of the two cultures were profound.'

God has much favoured me by letting me be born in this place, so beautiful and so different from all others. . . . Here the freedom and the way of life of every class seem to me admirable, perhaps unique in the world.'

Sagredo's love for Galileo, which is by itself an excellent testimonial, comes out clearly in the letter. 'Your departure,' he writes, 'produces an inconsolable unhappiness,' which cannot be compensated for by frequent correspondence. He is alarmed at the possible ill consequences of his friend's position at the court of an absolute monarch. Evil and envious men may sow suspicions in the Grand Duke's mind. He may for a time take pleasure in turning one of Galileo's telescopes on the city of Florence, but if it becomes necessary for him to study what goes on in other parts of Italy, in France, in Spain, in Germany, 'he will put your telescope aside. Even if by your skill you shall discover some other instrument useful for these new purposes,' who will ever be able to invent a spyglass for distinguishing madmen from the wise, good men from those of evil counsel, the ingenious architect from the obstinate and ignorant foreman? Sagredo ends up with a dig at the common foe, the unfortunate Jesuits. 'I am much disturbed,' he says, 'by your being in a place where the authority of the friends of the Jesuits counts heavily.' Mr Stillman Drake, with his usual balance and impartiality, remarks that Sagredo 'over-estimated the threat of interference by the Jesuits. . . . Many years elapsed before they turned against [Galileo], and then not without some provocation; at first his most effective support came from the scientists of that Society, and Galileo himself had a good opinion of these men.'[1]

Before he left Padua Galileo made one further telescopic discovery, the peculiar shape of the planet Saturn. It puzzled him because, though he boasted a little about the perfection of his telescope, it was not powerful enough to show Saturn's famous rings and much less any of its nine moons. He saw the planet as one large star flanked by two smaller ones almost touching it. After two years, in 1612,

Ronan Picture Library

Facsimile of Galileo's drawing of Saturn and its 'attendant stars'.

he started observing Saturn again, and what was his surprise to find the planet without its supporting stars and 'as perfectly round and sharply bounded as Jupiter'. He wondered to himself whether, as in the ancient myth, Saturn

[1] Stillman Drake, *Discoveries and Opinions of Galileo*, pp. 66-9. Was Galileo really in any greater danger in Florence than in Padua? When first the Inquisition began to trouble him, he could surely have slipped away to Switzerland or some other of the many places where its writ did not run. To dispose of another matter once and for all, it is hinted in nearly all the books, and more than hinted in Banfi, that the Jesuits, particularly the German Scheiner, precipitated the final trial and condemnation of Galileo. The Jesuit archives in Rome and other places have been diligently searched for some scintilla of evidence that this was so, but nothing involving Scheiner or any other Jesuit has ever been found.

had devoured his children, or whether, indeed, there was not, after all, some defect in the lenses of his telescope. 'Perhaps the day has arrived when languishing hope may be revived in those who, led by the most profound reflections, once plumbed the fallacies of all my new observations and found them to be incapable of existing!' After that glancing thrust at the Aristotelians, Galileo ventures to surmise that if Saturn is observed after the winter solstice of 1614, the attendant stars may once more be observed, and 'perhaps this planet also, no less than horned Venus, harmonises admirably with the great Copernican system, to the universal revelation of which doctrine propitious breezes are now seen to be directed towards us, leaving little fear of clouds or cross-wind.'[1]

Galileo's health suffered gravely on his return to Florence from 'the keen wintry air which proved a cruel enemy to my head and the rest of my body'. He had acquired his arthritis in Padua while exposed to the rigours of the December and January nights, but the air of his native land reduced him for the first three months to a state of abject misery, 'all the time indoors, even in bed, but without sleep or rest'. But his indomitable will asserted itself and in the brief intervals between one attack and another, he resumed his astronomical observations and even projected a visit of Copernican propaganda to Rome.

[1] Stillman Drake, *Discoveries and Opinions of Galileo*, pp. 143-4. Galileo was writing to his new friend Mark Welser of Augsburg, a wealthy member of a famous banking firm, a devout Catholic who was also keenly interested in scientific matters. The subject under discussion was sunspots and Galileo wrote from the pleasant villa of his friend Filippo Salviati who died young and whom he immortalized.

He took to announcing his new discoveries in very abstruse anagrams to friends such as Giuliano dei Medici and Kepler. Poor Kepler worried his head off trying to solve the puzzles. But on December 11, 1610, he received an easier anagram from Florence which gave him a tremendous thrill. It ran thus: *Cynthiae figuras aemulatur mater amorum*— The mother of love [Venus] emulates the shapes of Cynthia [the moon]. Galileo had discovered that Venus, like the moon, showed phases, from sickle (the 'horned Venus' of his letter to Welser) to full disc and back— a proof that the planet revolved round the sun. Copernicus had been puzzled by the apparent absence of phases in Venus, which planet he was able to study only with the naked eye. According to the heliocentric system it should have shown phases, yet, in spite of their seeming absence, Copernicus stuck to his guns, a fact which greatly impressed Galileo. His discovery also proved Ptolemy wrong in a vital part of his planetary theory. However, those who chose to adhere to Tycho Brahe's system were not put out of countenance by the fact that the mother of love waxed and waned.

Galileo had first visited Rome in 1587 when he was twenty-three and canvassing busily to secure the vacant chair of mathematics at the university of Bologna. He lost to Giovanni Antonio Magini who bore him a grudge for his intervention, but he won in Rome the friendship of a much greater man, a German from Bamberg named Christof Clau, better known as Christopher Clavius, chief professor of mathematics at the Jesuit Roman College, an institution founded by St Ignatius Loyola in 1552, and the direct ancestor of the present Pontifical Gregorian University, with its 2,500 students. Clavius is best known for the prominent part he played in the reform of the calendar carried out under Pope Gregory XIII, but he was also esteemed for his personal qualities as well as for his mathematics by many of the eminent men of his time. Though he never embraced Copernicanism and indeed had directly combated that theory in an edition of *The Sphere* by the medieval Joannes de Sacro Bosco, meaning John Hollywood, a Yorkshireman, which was the best exposition of the Ptolemaic astronomy in existence, that fact did not prevent Clavius and Galileo from becoming and remaining very good friends to the end of the Jesuit's life in 1612.

In December, 1610, Clavius informed Galileo that his colleagues at the Roman College, using a telescope perfected by Padre Lembo, had verified all his discoveries and added that 'in very truth you deserve great praise for being the first to make these observations'. Clavius was then in his seventies and his approbation meant a good deal to Galileo who was being attacked and threatened by a whole phalanx of Aristotelian backwoodsmen. At Pisa, the leading philosopher, Giulio Libri, refused all invitations to look through the telescope. Aristotle said nothing about Jupiter having moons, therefore the moons were a mere illusion. 'They are waiting,' wrote Galileo jocosely to Clavius, 'for me to find some means of bringing at least one of the four Medicean Planets down from the sky to earth to give an account of itself and clear up their doubts. Otherwise, it is no use for me to hope for their agreement.' Giulio Libri died in 1610 and Galileo then expressed a wry hope that as he would not look at Jupiter's satellites through the telescope, he would see them very plainly on his way to heaven!

The most obstinate of Galileo's foes was a large humourless person, unconnected with any university, named Ludovico delle Colombe. He took himself very seriously and, though without qualifications of any sort, wielded a good deal of influence, possibly through wealth. Why this man, of whom little is known, should have made such a dead set at Galileo is not certain. Yet he published one atrocious book after another to belittle him. Colombe in Italian means doves or pigeons, and Galileo guyed the antics of Ludovico and his kind by referring to them as 'The Pigeon League'. But the chief Pigeon was the first to take the sinister move of enlisting the scriptures against the new discoveries and their implied heliocentrism. He also addressed himself to Father Clavius, thanking him for having at first defended an unspotted moon; but he wrote too soon, for the eminent Jesuit went over completely to Galileo's view of that orb before he died the following year, 1612, at the age of seventy-six.

A Crusader in Rome

A Crusader in Rome

GALILEO would have gone to Rome in 1610 to see Clavius but for illness which compelled him to postpone his visit till March, 1611. That he went in the rôle of a crusader for Copernicanism was plain from his own avowal and from the collection of fine telescopes in his baggage. He must once and for all rescue the pope, the college of cardinals, and other eminent men in the Eternal City from their bondage to Aristotle and Ptolemy. He was uncommonly naïve and really ought to have known better at the age of forty-eight. In Rome, he soon discovered that the envy and hatred of the Aristotelians had gone ahead of him. It was rumoured that he had been expelled from Florence owing to the publication there of a confutation of *The Starry Messenger* by a good mathematician but idiotic scientist named Francesco Sizi, who was permitted to dedicate his lucubration to Prince Giovanni de' Medici. All that he had to do to kill such malicious talk was to make public the letters of warm recommendation which he bore to the Tuscan Ambassador and Cardinal del Monte from the Grand Duke. Cosimo spoke of him as 'il nostro amatissimo matematico'.

He arrived in Rome on March 29 and the following day turned his steps towards the Roman College, where he was relieved to find Clavius and his men laughing their heads off over Sizi's absurd book. On April 1 he wrote to the Tuscan Secretary of State, Belisario Vinta:

> I have had a long discussion with Fr Clavius and with two other most intelligent Fathers of the same Order. I found the pupils of these men occupied in reading, not without a great deal of laughter, the latest lucubrations which Signor Francesco Sizi has written and published against me. . . . The Fathers, being finally convinced that the Medicean planets are realities, have devoted the past two months to continuous observations of them, and these observations are still in progress. We have compared notes and have found that our experiences tally in every respect.[1]

That was a very good beginning to the chief mathematician's Roman campaign, but the sequel exceeded all his brightest expectations. He was lionized. Pope Paul V, the brusque and unpredictable canonist who had put the mighty republic of Venice under an interdict and was made by it to eat humble pie, a bad diet for popes, received the man of the hour in a long private audience and assured him of his unalterable good will. That, however, remained to be seen.

[1] Antonio Favaro, *Le Opere di Galileo Galilei*, Florence, 1890-1909, 20 vols., vol. xi, p. 79. This great work has been reprinted recently.

Ronan Picture

6. Tycho Brahe's celestial globe.

On April 6, Galileo was elected a member of the *Accademia dei Lincei*, the Academy of the Lynx-eyed, a very exclusive association for the study of science, founded shortly before by Federigo Cesi, son of the powerful Duke of Aquasparta. The importance of the academy, membership of which Galileo greatly prized, lay in the fact that in those days, as contrasted with our times, universities had become hidebound in conservatism, with a vested interest in maintaining the traditional views. Thus, not even in Padua was Galileo permitted to teach his Copernican convictions. The academies, of which several sprang up in imitation of the Lincean or for other purposes, offered an alternative to enterprising men. The constitution of the Lincean was published in 1624 and principles there set forth which have been emulated in other such organizations—for example, the English Royal Society—ever since:

The Lincean Academy desires as its members philosophers who are eager for real knowledge and will give themselves to the study of nature, especially mathematics; at the same time it will not neglect the ornaments of elegant literature and philology, which, like graceful garments, adorn the whole body of science. . . . It is not within the Lincean plan to find leisure for recitations and debates; the meetings will neither be frequent nor lengthy, and chiefly for the transaction of necessary business of the academy; but those who wish to enjoy such exercises will not be hindered in any way, so long as they perform them as incidental studies, decently and quietly, and not as vain promises and professions of how much they are about to do. For there is ample philosophical employment for everyone by himself, particularly if pains are taken in travelling and in the observation of natural phenomena and the book of nature which is always at hand; that is, the heavens and the earth.

... Let members add to their names the title of Lincean, which has been advisedly chosen as a caution and a constant stimulus, especially when they write on any literary subject, or in their private letters to associates, and in general when any work of theirs is wisely and well performed.

... The Linceans will pass over in silence all political controversies and every kind of quarrels and wordy disputes, especially gratuitous ones which give occasion to deceit, unfriendliness and hatred, as men who desire peace and seek to preserve their studies free from molestation and to avoid every sort of disturbance. And if anyone by command of his superiors or some other requirement shall be reduced to handling such matters, let them be printed without the name of Lincean, since they are alien to physical and mathematical science and hence to the object of the academy.[1]

Prince Cesi and Cardinal Farnese, both wealthy men, gave splendid banquets in honour of Galileo, who when the feasting and toasting were done produced one of his newly named telescopes and invited Cardinal Robert Bellarmine, among other distinguished guests, to view Jupiter's moons and other celestial phenomena for himself. That what he saw gave the gentle cardinal, now canonized and a doctor of the Church, food for thought is evident from the following inquiry which he addressed to Father Clavius and his colleagues at the Roman College on April 19, 1611:

[1] Quoted, with slight modifications, from a translation by John Elliot Drinkwater (— Bethune) in his *Life of Galileo*, published anonymously in London in 1829, p. 37. 'Although this is one of the earliest extensive biographies of Galileo, it is still one of the best' (Stillman Drake).

Very Reverend Fathers,

I know that your Reverences have heard of these new astronomical discoveries which an eminent mathematician has made by means of an instrument called a *cannone* or ocular tube. I myself by means of the same instrument have seen some very wonderful things concerning the moon and Venus, and I would be grateful if you would favour me with your honest opinion on the following matters:

1. Whether you confirm the report that there are multitudes of fixed stars invisible to the naked eye, and especially whether the Milky Way and the nebulae are to be regarded as collections of very small stars.

2. Whether it is true that Saturn is not a simple star but three stars joined together.

3. Whether it is a fact that Venus changes its shape, increasing and diminishing like the moon.

4. Whether the moon really has a rough and unequal surface.

5. Whether it is true that four movable stars revolve round Jupiter, each with a different movement from that of the others, but all the movements being exceedingly swift.

I am anxious to have some definite information about these matters, because I hear conflicting opinions expressed with regard to them. As your Reverences are skilled in the science of mathematics you will easily be able to tell me whether these new discoveries are well-founded, or whether they may not be a mere illusion. If you like you can write your answer on this same sheet.

Your Reverences' brother in Christ,
Robert Cardinal Bellarmine.

The professors' reply was in the following terms:

We give our answer in this sheet, as your lordship bade us, and we do so in the same order in which you proposed the questions.

1. It is true that the telescope reveals a vast number of stars in the nebulae of Cancer and the Pleiades, but it is not so certain that the Milky Way consists entirely of small stars. It seems more probable that there are parts of it which are denser and more continuous, though the existence of the many small stars cannot be denied. In fact, from what is to be seen in the nebulae of Cancer and the Pleiades, it may be conjectured that in the Milky Way, also, there are probably stars in immense multitudes, which cannot be discerned because they are too small.

2. We have observed that Saturn is not spherical in shape, as we perceive Jupiter and Mars to be, but oval, though we have not seen the two stars at the sides detached from the centre one in such a way that we might call them separate stars.

3. It is perfectly true that Venus diminishes and increases like the moon. During our observations of it when it was the evening star and almost full, we noticed that it grew less by gradual degrees on the illuminated side, which always faces towards the sun, and at the same time became ever more crescent-shaped. As the morning star, after conjunction with the sun, we perceived that it was horned and always presented its illuminated surface to the sun. This illumination continually increases while the apparent diameter of the planet gradually diminishes.

4. With regard to the moon, the great irregularities and inequalities of its surface cannot be denied, but Father Clavius is of opinion that these inequalities are merely apparent, being due to the fact that the lunar mass is not uniformly dense but composed of more rarefied and more solidified sections, which are the ordinary spots one sees with the naked eye. Others think that the surface of the moon is really unequal, but so far there is not sufficient evidence on this point to enable us to give a positive answer.

5. About Jupiter. Four stars may be seen revolving round that

planet with great rapidity—now, all four moving towards the east, now, all towards the west—while at times some of them move in one direction and some in the other, almost in a straight line. These objects cannot be fixed stars since their movements are far swifter and altogether different from the movements of the fixed stars. Moreover, their distance from one another and from Jupiter varies continually.

This is what we have to say in reply to your lordship's questions and, in conclusion, we offer you our humble respects, and pray God to grant you the fullest measure of happiness.[1]

Shortly after the dispatch of this reply, its writers, Father Christopher Clavius, Father Christopher Grienberger, Father Odo van Maelcote of Brussels, and Father John Paul Lembo, organized a public conference in honour of Galileo. Cardinals, princes, scientists, literary men, and scholars of every description, were invited to the Roman College where they found the man in the news installed like a king on a throne to listen to Father van Maelcote pronouncing an enthusiastic eulogy on the discoverer and his discoveries. The students of the college had been well coached in Galileo's views and expounded them to the distinguished assembly with a little too much gusto for the liking of the Aristotelians in the audience.

Among the speakers was a young Belgian Jesuit known as Gregory of St Vincent who became eminent himself in the domain of conic sections. He described the occasion half a century later to his friend the great Dutch scientist Chris-

---

[1] A. Favaro, *Le Opere di Galileo Galilei*, vol. xi, pp. 87-8, 92-3. Galileo saw to it that the answer to Bellarmine's inquiry became widely known.

tian Huygens. 'We proved clearly,' he wrote, 'that Venus revolves round the sun, but not without muttering from the philosophers'—*non absque murmure philosophorum.*

The murmuring was to grow in volume, in Rome as in Florence and other learned centres, with almost every day that passed until it drowned the voices of reason and responsibility, even among the cardinals.

Just before Galileo left Rome at the beginning of June Cardinal del Monte addressed a note to the Grand Duke of Tuscany telling of the great satisfaction his mathematician had given. 'Were we still living under the ancient Republic of Rome,' he ended, 'I verily believe that a column would have been erected on the Capitol in his honour.'[1]

But the eight cardinals of the Holy Office, among them Bellarmine, were more reserved in their attitude to the visitor from Florence. They were not at all concerned to question Galileo's remarkable astronomical discoveries, but may well have wondered whither this extraordinary man was heading in his persistent onslaughts by voice and pen on views accepted by the generality of mankind from time immemorial. They accordingly caused inquiry to be made in Padua whether Galileo's name had been mentioned in connection with the inquisitional investigations against his

[1] Karl von Gebler, *Galileo Galilei and the Roman Curia*, trans. by Mrs George Sturge, London, 1879, p. 10. This work by a young German officer of dragoons, who died at the age of twenty-eight, is by far the best account of the Galileo tragedy available in the English language. Gebler was a Protestant and had the strongest dislike for Jesuits, but his book, taken all in all, is strikingly impartial, as well as being scholarly and interesting in the highest degree. Its author's early death was a real catastrophe for learning.

Averroist friend Cesare Cremonini. It had not, and the investigations came to nothing owing to the opposition of the state.

It may have been all the excitement in Rome caused by Galileo's visit that inspired St Robert Bellarmine to have a faulty sundial, set in one of the outer walls of his residence, mended. As appeared in his little book, *The Ascent of the Mind to God*, he was much interested in the movement of the sun. The gnomon or pin of the dial had become twisted out of position, so the Cardinal asked Father Grienberger of the Roman College to come and see whether anything could be done about it. Grienberger brought with him one of the brightest of his students in mathematics named Orazio Grassi, who was destined to be given a kind of black immortality in the most brilliant and merciless of Galileo's polemical writings, *The Assayer—Il Saggiatore*. Poor Grassi did not altogether deserve his slaughtering, but he should have had more sense than to enter into argument with the most deadly controversialist of his age. It is he who tells the story of the sundial. Having examined it, they informed the cardinal that it could be put right at a cost of two *giulii*. When the old man heard this, his face fell and he remained silent for a moment. Then he said: 'I have not the heart to spend so much on my own convenience, for two *giulii* is enough money to support some poor wretch for two days.'

So the sundial remained unmended and some mendicant got the money thus saved. It is a trifling story, but it reveals a disposition perhaps more precious than all Galileo's fine mathematics. Galileo loved to score off people and to make them look silly, which was a frame of mind quite incomprehensible to St Robert Bellarmine.

After his return to Florence, Galileo became involved with the diehard Aristotelians in a matter of physics rather than astronomy. His telescopic discoveries had convinced the Roman Jesuits that Aristotle's views on the unchangeability of the heavens, his perfect moon, and his system of crystal spheres carrying the celestial bodies, were no longer tenable. The skies were far more complicated than they, with the rest of mankind, barring a few erratic geniuses, had suspected; but they were not yet ready to go the whole way with Galileo and Copernicus. Now, the principal mathematician and philosopher to the Grand Duke of Tuscany came right down to this earth, which he already firmly believed to be a planet like Venus or Saturn, though he could not strictly prove it in a way to convince the Jesuits or anybody except Kepler and his own devoted disciples, and Kepler did not need any convincing.

The Grand Duke liked to give public dinners to which were invited distinguished men and women. It was hot on one such occasion and ice had obviously been provided, for the conversation turned on the reason why that substance floats. According to Aristotle and his seventeenth-century disciples, the floating or sinking of bodies immersed in water depended largely on their shape. Galileo, who was present, had long devoted his splendid talents to this problem and maintained strongly the opinion attributed to the great Sicilian Archimedes, who is supposed to have sprung from his bath and rushed through the streets shout-

CVSSINO
CATEDRA
CAPELLANO
SECRETARII
CERNO
CORNV
LA CANDELA
CERIVM ALBVM
PATRIARCA

Museo Correr.

7. Section of a woodcut by Mattia Pagan, showing the procession of the Doge of Venice in St. Mark's Square on Palm Sunday.

8. Pope Paul V, 1605–1621.

ing 'Eureka!' when he hit upon it. It was that bodies float because their weight is less than that of the volume of water which they displace.

Two visiting cardinals from Rome graced this particular banquet, one of whom, Maffeo Barberini, sided entirely with Galileo against the outraged Aristotelians at table. From that moment Barberini and Galileo became fast friends. History sometimes takes ironical turns, for it was this cardinal who, more than twenty years later, as Pope Urban VIII, brought about the disastrous condemnation of Galileo by the Roman Inquisition. Grand Duke Cosimo was so much impressed by the brilliant argumentation of his mathematician that he requested him to put it into a book. This he had ready in his excellent Italian by the following spring (1612), calling the book a *Discourse on Things that Float or Move on Water*. He at once sent a presentation copy to Cardinal Bellarmine and received the following reply:

Illustrious Signore,

I have received your letter and the accompanying treatise on bodies that move about or remain still when placed in water. I shall read it with much pleasure, sure as I am that it is a work worthy of so eminent an author. While thanking you most heartily for your courtesy in sending it to me, I would like to assure you that the affection you have thus shown me is fully reciprocated on my part, and you will see that this is so, if ever I get an opportunity of doing you a service. With my kindest respects and a prayer that God may grant you every blessing.[1]

[1] A. Favaro, *Le Opere di Galileo Galilei*, vol. xi, pp. 337-8.

St Robert Bellarmine was not the man to indulge in empty compliments and promises. Three years later when Galileo got himself into trouble with the Roman Inquisition he did the impatient genius, whose splendid talents and deep Catholic faith he fully appreciated, an inestimable service. Bellarmine, though naturally conservative and bred to revere Aristotle's view, repudiated a key concept of that master, the idea that the heavenly bodies from the moon and beyond were composed of a quintessence, simple, incorruptible and constantly moving in a circle. Though he had lectured on astrology in his youth as a subject of great contemporary concern, he never believed in it, despite the example of Pope Paul III who gave the Jesuits the freedom of the Church and kept a private astrologer at the Vatican. Bellarmine was no scientist in the Galilean sense of the word, but neither was he, even in scientific matters, anybody's fool.

In reading the *Discourse on Floating Bodies*, the cardinal may have been disconcerted by Galileo's mockery of the unfortunate professors whose arguments he turned inside out, giving them new force, adding others that had not occurred to them, and then bringing the whole house of cards tumbling about their heads by his own brilliant demonstrations. It understandably made them wild, and no book of his was attacked by them more often or more savagely, Ludovico delle Colombe always in the lead. To make people into laughing-stocks is not the way to convert them.

Sunspots were the next objects to engage Galileo's attention. They were very active at this time and many astronomers besides the great man of Florence had been studying them. One was a Jesuit professor of mathematics at the university of Ingolstadt in Bavaria named Christopher Scheiner who, though a good enough scientist, was a man of irascible and contentious temper. He made known his findings in a series of letters to his friend Mark Welser, wealthy member of a famous Augsburg banking family who also was a devout Catholic and a very enthusiastic and open-minded amateur of science.

Welser promptly published Scheiner's letters and sent a copy of the book to Galileo asking for his views. He wrote in excellent Italian, and Galileo felt entitled to reply in the same language, which unfortunately Scheiner did not know. Scheiner's observation of the sunspots was skilful but his interpretation of them was lamentable. He was badly hampered in his investigations by out-of-date belief in that prime Aristotelian dogma, the immaculacy and immutability of the sun and other heavenly bodies. Surely, he must have read *The Starry Messenger* which was in Latin and had disposed for ever of that peculiar piece of imagination. The spots, he suggested, were in fact small stars or clusters of stars circling round the sun. Galileo, who was impeded by no scruple for immaculacy, proved that the spots could not be stars, that they were close to the surface of the sun, and that that great luminary turned on its axis just as did the earth. In his third enormous letter to Mark Welser, who had meantime himself been elected to the Lincean Academy but, alas, died shortly afterwards from gout, Galileo writes rather grandly that neither he nor so far as he knows anyone else has pretended that the sunspots are lakes or caverns in the body of the sun. That is precisely what sunspots are, which goes to show that even Galileo could be mistaken.

His three great letters were published in their original Italian in Rome by the Lincean Academy in 1613, right under the noses of the pope and his cardinals. He declared openly in the book for heliocentrism, not as a hypothesis but as physical fact, and predicted its forthcoming universal triumph. As the book was in Italian it must have been widely read, yet no cardinal nor bishop nor other person of any consequence in Rome raised the slightest objection.

In his book Galileo treated Scheiner, whom he knew only under the pseudonym of Apelles, with unusual courtesy, but he could not refrain from girding at his Aristotelian foes: 'They wish never to raise their eyes from those pages [Aristotle's]—as if this great book of the universe had been written to be read by nobody but Aristotle, and his eyes destined to see for all posterity.'

He thought that the discovery of the sunspots and of the rotation of the sun might well be, as he wrote to a friend, 'the funeral, or rather the last judgment, of pseudo-philosophy'. But his Paduan friend, Paolo Gualdo, whom he trusted, wrote him the following warning in May, 1612: 'As to this matter of the earth turning round, I have found hitherto no philosopher or astrologer who is willing to subscribe to the opinion of your honour, and much less a theologian; be pleased therefore to consider carefully before you publish this opinion assertively, for many things can be uttered by way of disputation which it is not wise to affirm.'[1] This was the identical advice which Cardinal Bellarmine tendered to Galileo, but he did not heed it; and hence the tragedy.

[1] Cited in Santillana, *The Crime of Galileo*, University of Chicago Press, 1955, p. 25. This is an exhilarating book to read, if, perhaps, a little more severe towards St Robert Bellarmine and his Jesuit brethren than the documents warrant. The Jesuits were men of their age and not prophetic geniuses like Galileo. Besides, they were under authority and could not teach anything they liked; even though in their secret hearts they may very well have inclined to Galileo's conclusion.

Religion and Science

Religion and Science

On December 13, 1613, eight months or so after the publication of the *History and Demonstrations Concerning Sunspots and their Phenomena*, Grand Duke Cosimo invited several learned men to a banquet in Pisa, where the court was then staying. Galileo was himself ill and in bed at the time but his closest friend and most enthusiastic disciple, the Cassinese Benedictine monk Benedetto Castelli, for whom he had secured the chair of mathematics at Pisa, was among the guests. He was thirty-five at this time and growing in reputation as a scientist with every year that passed. No love was lost between the Benedictines and the Jesuits of that period owing to controversy about the *Spiritual Exercises* of St Ignatius, which, the Benedictines maintained, Ignatius had borrowed from the *Ejercitatorio* of Garcia Cisneros, Abbot of Monserrat. Thus in 1595, Dom Arnaldo

Wion of the Great Abbey of St Gregory, Douai, from which Downside is lineally descended, published at Venice two large tomes on Benedictine origins and history. Speaking of the *Ejercitatorio* of Cisneros, he wrote: 'From that work the Reverend Fathers of the Society of Jesus have borrowed their method of meditation and all the perfection of their Order.' The Reverend Fathers did not take too kindly to this interpretation of their constitutions, which is seriously erroneous, and bad blood was made to such an extent that in the long run Rome had to intervene, and slap the two principal contenders on to the Index in 1645, and leave them there till the year 1900. It is a well known fact that someone fed Galileo with suspicions against the Jesuits, and who more likely than Benedetto Castelli, his great Benedictine friend?

Castelli, who may be considered the father of hydrostatics, was an admirable man, living cheerfully on a shoestring and pursuing his work at Pisa under the most hampering circumstances. He had been won to the Copernican cause at Padua where he first came to know Galileo, but he was strictly forbidden by the overseer of the university, Arturo d'Elci, to air any of his heliocentric views at Pisa, even apart from his public lectures. It was Castelli who edited and published under his own name Galileo's replies to the attacks on his book, *The Discourse on Floating Bodies*, and towards the end of the year 1613 he became involved in an event which was to be of crucial importance in Galileo's entire career. The following is his account of it, written to Galileo on December 14, 1613:

Wednesday morning I was dining at the Court when I was

asked about the university by the Grand Duke. I gave him a detailed account of things, with which he showed himself well satisfied. Then he asked me if I had a telescope, to which I replied yes, and fell to talking of my observations of the Medicean planets made the previous night. Madame Christina[1] wanted to know their position, and thereupon the talk turned to the necessity of their being real objects and not illusions of the telescope. Their Highnesses asked Professor Boscaglia[2] about this, and he replied that their existence could not be denied. I then contributed all that I knew and could tell them about Your Excellency's wonderful discovery and establishment of the orbits of these planets. Don Antonio de' Medici,[3] who was present at the table, beamed at me and showed himself well pleased by what I said. After much talk, which went off quite solemnly, dinner was finally over and I left. But I had hardly come out of the palace when Madame Christina's porter overtook me and told me that she wished me to return. Now before I tell you what ensued you must first know that while we were at table Dr Boscaglia had had the ear of Madame for a while; and, conceding as true all the new things you have discovered in the sky, he said that only the motion of the earth had something incredible in it and could not take place, in particular because the holy scripture was obviously contrary to this view.

Now, getting back to my story, I entered into the chambers of Her Highness, and there I found the Grand Duke, Madame Christina and the Archduchess,[4] Don Antonio, Don Paolo

[1] Christina of Lorraine, mother of the Grand Duke Cosimo II.

[2] Cosimo Boscaglia, a special professor of philosophy at the University of Pisa, expounder of Plato and a favourite of the Grand Duke among men of letters there.

[3] Not truly one of the Medici, but accepted as a sort of honorary cousin by Cosimo II.

[4] Maria Madeleine of Austria, wife of Cosimo. She is referred to by her Austrian title of Archduchess, the honorary title of Grand Duchess remaining to Christina, her mother-in-law.

Giordano (Orsini),[1] and Dr Boscaglia. Madame began, after some questions about myself, to argue the holy scripture against me. Thereupon, after having made suitable disclaimers. I commenced to play the theologian with such assurance and dignity that it would have done you good to hear me. Don Antonio assisted me, giving me such heart that instead of being dismayed by the majesty of Their Highnesses I carried things off like a paladin. I quite won over the Grand Duke and his Archduchess, while Don Paolo came to my assistance with a very apt quotation from the scripture. Only Madame Christina remained against me, but from her manner I judged that she did this merely to hear my replies. Professor Boscaglia said never a word.[2]

On December 21, 1613, Galileo sent Gastelli a huge letter containing his opinions on the proper relations of science and religion. It was in the following terms:

The holy scriptures cannot err and the decrees therein contained are absolutely true and inviolable. But I should in your place have added that, though scripture cannot err, its expounders and interpreters are liable to err in many ways; and one error in particular would be most grave and most frequent, if we always stopped short at the literal signification of the words. For in this wise not only many contradictions would be apparent, but grave heresies and blasphemies. For then it would be necessary to give God hands and feet and

---

[1] It was to this member of the powerful Orsini family that Scheiner later dedicated his *Rosa Ursina*, which included the bitterest personal attack ever made against Galileo, and Orsini was much distressed when he learned what was in the book. His brother, Alessandro Orsini, became a cardinal in 1615, and shortly thereafter urged the pope strongly to rule in favour of Galileo's views—an interview which resulted instead in their prohibition.

[2] A. Favaro, *Le Opere di Galileo Galilei*, vol. xi, pp. 65-6.

ears, and human and bodily emotions such as anger,
repentance, hatred and sometimes forgetfulness of things past,
and ignorance of the future. And in scripture there are found
many propositions which, taking the bare sense of the words,
appear contrary to the truth, but they are placed there in
such wise in order to accommodate themselves to the capacity
of the vulgar; so that for those few who merit to be separated
from the plebeian crowd, it is necessary for wise expositors
to produce the true meaning and to explain the particular
reasons for which they have been thus worded. It being laid
down, therefore, that scripture is not only capable of divers
interpretations, but that in many places it requires an interpretation differing from the apparent meaning of the words,
it seems to me that in mathematical disputes it must be interpreted according to the latter mode. Holy scripture and nature
are both emanations from the divine word: the former
dictated by the Holy Spirit, the latter the executrix of God's
commands.

Holy scripture has to be accommodated to the common
understanding in many things which differ in reality from
the terms used in speaking of them. But nature, being on the
contrary inexorable and immutable, and caring not one jot
whether her secret reasons and modes of operation be above
or below the capacity of men's understanding: it appears
that, as she never transgresses her own laws, those natural
effects which the experience of the senses places before our
eyes, or which we infer from adequate demonstration, are
in no wise to be revoked because of certain passages in scripture, which may be turned and twisted into a thousand
different meanings.... Scripture has not abstained from veil-
ing in shadow its principal dogmas, attributing to God himself conditions differing from, and contrary to, the divine
essence. And who can assert or sustain that, in speaking
incidentally of the sun, or of the earth, or of other created
bodies, scripture should have elected to restrain itself

rigorously to the literal significance of the words used? . . .
It being manifest that two truths cannot be contrary to each
other, it becomes the office of wise expounders to labour till
they find how to make these passages of holy writ concordant
with those conclusions, of which either necessary demonstration or the evidence of our senses have made us sure and certain. . . . As we cannot be certain that the interpreters are
all divinely inspired, I think it would be prudent if men were
forbidden to employ passages of scripture for the purpose of
sustaining what our senses or demonstrated proof may
manifest to the contrary. Who can set bounds to the mind
of man? Who dare assert that he already knows all that in
this universe is knowable? And on this account, beyond the
articles concerning salvation and the stability of the faith,
against the unchangeableness of which there is no danger
of any valid and efficacious innovations being introduced,
it would perhaps be best to counsel that none should be added
unnecessarily; and if it be so, how much greater the disorder
to add to these articles at the demand of persons, who
though they may be divinely inspired, yet we see clearly that
they are destitute of the intelligence necessary not merely
to disprove, but to understand those demonstrations by which
scientific conclusions are confirmed.

I believe that the intention of holy writ was to persuade
men of the truths necessary for salvation, such as neither
science nor any other means could render credible, but only
the voice of the Holy Spirit. But I do not think it necessary
to believe that the same God who gave us our senses, our
speech, our intellect, would have put aside the use of these,
to teach us instead such things as with their help we could
find out for ourselves, particularly in the case of these sciences
of which there is not the smallest mention in the scriptures;
and, above all, in astronomy, of which so little notice is taken
that the names of none of the planets are mentioned. Surely
if the intention of the sacred writers had been to teach the

people astronomy, they would not have passed over the subject so completely.[1]

What an astonishing person Galileo was to be able to improvise readily a letter such as that. He was never much of a reader of books, yet he shows an uncommonly close acquaintance with the text of the scriptures and, still more remarkably, with the interpretations of the Fathers of the Church, especially St Augustine in his *De Genesi ad Litteram*. Castelli was his closest ecclesiastical friend, but he is writing to Castelli and therefore it cannot be he who put him on to St Augustine and the other Fathers he cites. This competence, in a field so different from the one he had chosen, is one of the many mysteries of his genius. He was better acquainted with recent commentators on the scriptures than Bellarmine himself and was able to quote for St Robert's benefit the view of a Spanish Jesuit, Benedict Pereira, who died in Rome in 1610, to the following effect:

> In dealing with the doctrine of Moses we must be careful to avoid saying confidently and without reservation anything which contradicts manifest experiences and the reasonings of natural philosophy or the other sciences. Since every truth is in harmony with all other truth, the truth of holy writ cannot be opposed to the solid reasons and findings of human knowledge.

Bellarmine must have known Pereira but he did not entirely share his readiness to make concessions to the scientists.

[1] Translation, Mary Allan Olney, *The Private Life of Galileo*, London, 1870, pp. 73 seq. See below p. 118 for more about this book.

79

Galileo, well knowing that the scriptural issue could be crucial in his endeavours to win acceptance for Copernicanism, set himself to revise and strengthen his letter to Castelli and addressed the new version to the lady responsible for bringing the question to a head. It is known as the *Letter to the Grand Duchess Christina* and was finished probably about June of that same year as the letter to Castelli, 1615.

Throughout his great letter to Castelli and the revised version of it addressed to Duke Cosimo's mother, the Grand Duchess Christina of Lorraine, Galileo assumes, without explicitly saying so, the physical reality of Copernicanism. He also maintains that it is not his business but that of the commentators and theologians to disprove it by arguments as good as those then available for its establishment, by which he meant largely his own discoveries of the moons of Jupiter, the phases of Venus, and the changeable nature and rotation of the sun. Those discoveries had certainly wrecked and ruined Aristotle's and Ptolemy's conceptions of the heavens but they still fell short in the one all-important respect of establishing the Copernican conception. If in actual physical fact the earth was in motion round the sun, as the moon is certainly in motion round the earth, then one or other of the 'fixed' stars ought to show annually an apparent infinitesimal displacement of position called parallax. Copernicus and Galileo knew this very well and were distressed that they had not the means to determine a star's annual parallax. It was not until the nineteenth century that the great German astronomer

Friedrich Bessel determined after years of patient observation the parallax of the star 61 in the constellation of the Swan, and so put the physical reality of heliocentrism beyond dispute.

Nevertheless, Galileo was certainly entitled to regard the discoveries of his telescope as a convergence of strong probabilities affording a reasonable proof of the physical reality of heliocentrism. But he was perhaps a little disingenuous in his attempt to shift the burden of disproof on to the shoulders of the theologians and in trying to manoeuvre them into a position they had not tried to maintain. Copernicanism, he insisted obliquely, must be accepted as physical fact, or else altogether repudiated as detestable heresy. What the theologians, and particularly Cardinal Bellarmine, maintained all along was a third position, that the heliocentric theory could freely be held and discussed as a *hypothesis*, even as a better hypothesis to explain the appearances than that of the traditional Ptolemy.

The reason why Bellarmine and others who thought with him espoused the idea of Copernicanism as a hypothesis was that the book of the Polish Canon, *De Revolutionibus Orbium Coelestium, On the Revolutions of the Heavenly Orbs,* bore a reassuring preface in Latin which stated that 'the author of the book had done nothing deserving of reprehension, as it is the business of an astronomer to calculate the movements of the heavens by diligent and ingenious observation, and then to excogitate and invent various hypotheses to account for the movements, so that by the principles of geometry they may be

81

explained in the past and foretold in the future'. The writer of the preface goes on to say that the real causes of the movements are utterly beyond the author's discovery. From all this it should surely have been apparent to Cardinal Bellarmine and everyone else who read the preface that it was not Copernicus himself writing. Strange to say they missed the point. But Galileo did not and trumpeted the fact loudly, though not he but Kepler discovered the forger's name and revealed it in a book of his which did not see the light until the nineteenth century.

He was a very eminent Protestant theologian of Nuremberg where the book of Copernicus was printed under his direction. In the fashion of the time he had graecized his name of Heiligmann into Osiander. He corresponded with Copernicus, whom he warmly admired and in whose heliocentrism he firmly believed, but he did not ask his permission to write the preface nor did he submit it to him, knowing that it would be rejected out of hand, as Copernicus was convinced of the physical reality of heliocentrism. The preface was a piece of well-meant but misguided diplomacy. Osiander had quarrelled with Luther and his great lieutenant Melanchthon over the question of justification, and knew that both men were determinedly opposed to the Copernican theory, widely known long before the book was published, on scriptural grounds. By declaring that the theory was merely a mathematician's hypothesis, claiming no physical reality, he hoped to placate the two stalwarts of Wittenberg, and that thus Copernicus might be accorded a hearing in Germany as elsewhere. His bogus preface was enormously successful, for it reassured both Catholics and Protestants, and poor Copernicus never knew of the trick that had been played on him, as he was dying when the first copy of the *De Revolutionibus* was brought to him in 1543.

Galileo had many good friends in Rome as in Florence, but none more devoted than the sharp-tongued artist Ludovico Cardi da Cigoli. On December 16, 1611, this man wrote to him while he was engaged in Florence on his *Discourse on Floating Bodies*, in the following terms:

> I have been told by a friend of mine, a priest who is very fond of you, that a certain crowd of ill-disposed men envious of your virtue and merits met at the house of the archbishop there and put their heads together in a mad quest for any means by which they could damage you, either with regard to the motion of the earth or otherwise. One of them wished to have a preacher state from the pulpit that you were asserting outlandish things. The priest, having perceived the animosity against you, replied as a good Christian and a religious man ought to do. Now I write this to you so that your eyes will be open to such envy and malice on the part of that sort of evil-doers.

The archbishop referred to was the archbishop of Florence, Mgr Marzimedici, who is stated by Galileo's beloved pupil and first biographer, Vincenzo Viviani, to have been one of his disciples. The fact that Galileo's enemies met at his house does not necessarily mean that he had any sympathy with them. Galileo was himself suffering greatly from the severe winter climate of Florence at this time and gladly accepted the invitation of his friend Filippo Salviati to stay with him at his Villa delle Selve to the west of the city. There he remained while writing his *Letters on Sunspots* during the year 1612.

He had been left comparatively in peace by his enemies during this time, but towards the end of the year he learned that his views had been assailed in Florence by a Dominican priest named Niccolò Lorini. This apparently was the first time he had been criticized by an ecclesiastic and he rather arrogantly demanded an explanation. Lorini, a much-esteemed Florentine patrician aged seventy, might reasonably have told him to mind his own business, as the discussion at which he had spoken was a private one and no affair of his. Instead, he replied very courteously and pacifically as follows:

> Please know, your excellency, that the suspicion of my having entered into a discussion of philosophical matters against anyone on All Souls' Day is completely false and without foundation. It is not only untrue, but not even probable, as I have never strayed from my line and duty. I have never dreamed of getting involved in such matters, nor have I so much as mentioned them to Signor Pandolfini or anybody else, so I am at a loss to know what grounds there can be for such a suspicion, this thing having never occurred to me. It is indeed true that I, not in order to argue but merely to avoid appearing a blockhead when the discussion was started by others, did say a few words just to show I was alive. I said, as I still say, that this opinion of Ipernicus, or whatever his name is, would appear to be hostile to the divine scripture. But it is of little consequence to me, for I have other things to do; for me it is enough that no occasion shall be given to anyone for believing us what we are not. For I am confident that all our nobility is steadfastly Catholic. . . .[1]

[1] A. Favaro, *Le Opere di Galileo Galilei*, vol. xi, p. 247.

The Pandolfini mentioned was a young public official, and as a pupil and good friend of Galileo appears to have informed him about some discussion at which he was present. Lorini's courteous reply was wasted on Galileo who jibed at him in a letter to Prince Cesi:

> Here in Florence there is a clumsy speaker, who has decided to detest the mobility of the earth, but this good fellow is so unfamiliar with the author of that doctrine that he calls him *Ipernicus*. Behold whence and by whom poor philosophy is subject to extortion!

But Galileo (one almost feels inclined to say, 'serve him right!') had by no means finished with Lorini yet. Benedetto Castelli had unwisely caused many copies of Galileo's letter to him on science and religion to be made and distributed. Old Father Lorini on a visit to Pisa came upon a copy and was profoundly shocked by its contents. Back at his convent of San Marco among the exquisite frescoes of Fra Angelico, Lorini discussed the offending letter with his brethren, and in their name addressed the following letter to Cardinal Paolo Sfondrati, Secretary of the Holy Office, at Rome on February 7, 1615:

> All our Fathers of this devout convent of St Mark are of opinion that the letter contains many propositions which appear to be suspect or presumptuous, as when it asserts that the language of holy scripture does not mean what it seems to mean; that in discussions about natural phenomena the last and lowest place ought to be given to the authority of the sacred text; that its commentators have very often erred in their interpretation; that the holy scriptures should not be mixed up with anything except matters of religion. . . .

85

When I saw that this document was in everybody's hands ... that [the disciples of Galileo] were taking upon themselves to expound the holy scriptures according to their private lights and in a manner different from that of the common interpretation of the Fathers of the Church; that they strove to defend an opinion which appeared to be quite contrary to the sacred text; that they spoke in slighting terms of the ancient Fathers, and of St Thomas Aquinas; that they were treading underfoot the entire philosophy of Aristotle which has been of such service to scholastic theology; and, in fine, that to show their cleverness they were airing and scattering broadcast in our steadfastly Catholic city a thousand saucy and irreverent surmises; when, I say, I became aware of all this, I made up my mind to acquaint your Lordship with the state of affairs, that you in your holy zeal for the faith may, in conjunction with your illustrious colleagues, provide such remedies as will appear advisable.[1]

Just seven weeks before the dispatch of Lorini's letter, with a copy enclosed of Galileo's science and faith letter to Castelli, the prime villain of the whole of this story came storming on to the scene. He, too, was a Florentine Dominican, Fra Tommáso Caccini, of the beautiful Dominican priory of Santa Maria Novella. The Galilean praetorian guard have no epithets violent enough for this strange priest, and he certainly deserved most of them. He was a fiery preacher, addicted to sensationalism, and unscrupulous in the methods he employed to attain his ends. In fact, leaving out the genius and the style, he closely resembled Galileo! It was the good custom in Florence in those days to expound the entire bible in church during the course of every few years. On the fourth Sunday in

[1] A. Favaro, *Galileo e l'inquisizione*, Florence, 1907, pp. 37-8.

Advent in the year 1614, which fell on December 21, the tenth chapter of the Book of Joshua had been reached at Santa Maria Novella in which occurs the famous passage:

   ' "Sun, stand thou still at Gibeon,
     and thou moon in the valley of Ajalon."
  And the sun stood still and the moon stayed,
     until the nation took vengeance on their enemies.'

Fra Tommáso seized on the passage with avidity to denounce in unmeasured terms the Copernican views then being widely and rather insolently aired in Florence by Galileo's disciples. There is no evidence that Caccini was the mouth-piece of the Aristotelian faction. He appears to have acted entirely on his own responsibility and it is quite certain that the notorious sermon had nothing whatever to do with Galileo's science and religion letter to Castelli of exactly a year earlier. Caccini did not even know of the existence of this letter. He made a savage attack on mathematicians in general, describes their science as '*l'arte diabolica della matematica*' and expressed a wish that they should be banished from all Christian countries as fomenters of ungodliness. The silly man had just enough sense not to mention Galileo by name.

The sermon shocked Caccini's religious brethren and they denounced him to the Master-General of the Dominican Order in Rome, Fra Luigi Maraffi, who had a deep respect and even admiration for Galileo's great qualities. He promptly and wholeheartedly apologized for Caccini's outburst:

I have been extremely annoyed by this scandal caused by a member of my Order. It is my misfortune to have to answer for all the stupidities which some of the thirty or forty thousand of my brethren in religion may and actually do commit.[1]

Matteo Caccini, Tommáso's brother, a curial official in Rome, addressed him a blistering letter, in which he referred to an earlier escapade in Bologna :

Was it not enough for you to get yourself into that previous scrape? Brother Thomas, take it from me, reputation rules the world, and people who are responsible for such stupidities as yours lose their good names ... you have committed a gross blunder and made a dreadful fool of yourself. ...

Brother Thomas didn't care. He was in the limelight and apparently loved it. Benedetto Castelli, O.S.B., referred to Caccini and his kind as 'pickpockets and highwaymen who waylay mathematicians', and with Galileo himself he became a positive obsession.

Hard upon Caccini's atrocious sermon had come Lorini's acquisition of a copy of the letter to Castelli. Galileo had reason for alarm and decided to transmit an authentic version of his letter to one of his most trusted counsellors in Rome, Mgr Piero Dini, Archbishop of Fermo. With it went the following covering letter, dated February 16, 1615 :

Since these fathers and especially the man who spoke against me [at Santa Maria Novella] have, as I am told, made another move with regard to my letter [to Castelli], I thought

---

[1] A. Favaro, *Le Opere di Galileo Galilei*, vol. xii, p. 127.

it would be well to send your reverence an accurate copy of it. You would oblige me very much by reading it to Father Grienberger, that excellent mathematician and my very dear friend and patron. If you consider it advisable, you might also find some opportunity of bringing it to the notice of Cardinal Bellarmine, as I am given to understand that these Dominican Fathers are proposing to apply to his Lordship, in the hopes of securing at least the condemnation of the book and teaching of Copernicus. . . .

Galileo was well advised to send that special copy of his letter, for Lorini's copy, transmitted to Cardinal Sfondrati, had been interfered with by some miscreant who changed two words to make it seem more objectionable. These were the only words in the long letter to which the consultor of the Holy Office, almost certainly a Dominican, objected when the letter was submitted to him by Cardinal Sfondrati. The letter as a whole he found to be quite in accordance with Catholic teaching on the scriptures, 'even if the wording was too sharp in places'. This was an excellent retort to the 'fundamentalist' Lorini.

Archbishop Dini had to delay his reply to Galileo until March 7, for reasons which he states in the following letter:

The thousand spectacles and other celebrations during these days of carnival have prevented me from finding the persons with whom I desired to have audience. However, I made up for the delay by having several copies of your letter to Father Castelli transcribed. One of these I afterwards presented to Father Grienberger, and at the same time read to him the letter which you had addressed to myself. Several other people have had copies presented to them also, and I had a long conversation with Cardinal Bellarmine about the matters you mentioned.

He assured me that since you and he had discussed the astronomical question together, he had never once heard it ventilated in any way. As to Copernicus, his Lordship said that he could not believe that his work would be forbidden, and that the worst that could happen to it would, in his opinion, be the insertion of a note stating that the theory was introduced to save the celestial appearances, or some similar expression, in the same way as epicycles had been introduced. With this reservation, he continued, you would be at liberty to speak on these matters whenever you had occasion to do so. Concerning the matters themselves, it seemed to him that the passage of holy scripture most opposed to the new interpretation of the celestial phenomena was the psalmist's text, *Exultavit ut gigas ad currendam viam*, together with the words that follow, as all commentators up to the present time have understood it to imply that the sun is in motion. I answered that the holy scriptures might be considered in this place as simply employing our usual form of speech, but the Cardinal said that in dealing with such a question we must not be too hasty, just as it would not be right to rush into condemnation of anyone for holding the views which I had put before him. He added that if you had given any cogent reasons in your letter for those views, he would be very pleased to study them. . . .

Then he told me that he intended to invite Father Grienberger to his house that he might discuss the question with him, and this very morning I have been to visit the Father, to see if there was any further news. I found that there was nothing fresh except that Father Grienberger would have been better pleased if you had first given your proofs before beginning to speak about the holy scriptures. I answered him that if you had done this, you would have been taken to task for giving your own facts preference, in the discussion, to the word of God. As for the arguments which I put forward on behalf of your views, the Father said that he doubted whether they were not more plausible than true. . . .[1]

Meantime, on February 28, another devoted friend of Galileo in Rome, a young priest and curial official named Giovanni Ciàmpoli, wrote to tell him that he had had a conversation with Cardinal Maffeo Barberini, the future Pope Urban VIII. The letter was in the following terms:

The Lord Cardinal Barberini who, as you know by experience, has always admired your genius, told me only yesterday evening that he thought it would be the more prudent course in dealing with these matters not to go beyond the reasons given by Ptolemy or Copernicus, nor to employ any other except physical and mathematical arguments. The theologians consider that it is their province to expound the sacred scriptures, and besides, when a new idea is brought to the fore, even though this be done with admirable skill, not everyone has a heart so free from prejudice as to be ready to accept the arguments for what they are worth. They become so exaggerated and distorted in their passage from mouth to mouth that the man who first uttered them would eventually be unable to recognize them as his own.

I know this right well. Your views on the phenomena of the moon attribute to that globe a certain similarity with our earth. This point is seized on and exaggerated by somebody. Soon you are supposed to have taught that there are men on the moon. Now another man comes along and wants to know how these lunar people can be shown to have descended from Adam or to have issued from the ark of Noah. . . .

You will pardon me in your kindness for the seeming

[1] A. Favaro, *Le Opere di Galileo Galilei*, vol. viii, pp. 354-5.

impertinence of these hints which I give you, as you know that they proceed from the very deep affection which I bear you.[1]

Three weeks later the same Ciàmpoli reported that Archbishop Dini and himself had had an interview with Cardinal del Monte, a Tuscan and brother of Galileo's old friend the Marchese Guidobaldo del Monte:

> Cardinal del Monte told us that he had discussed the question of Copernicanism at great length with Cardinal Bellarmine, and that they had concluded as follows. If you treat the system of Copernicus and set forth its proofs without bringing in the scriptures, the interpretation of which is the business of qualified theologians, then you should not be opposed in any way whatever. . . .
>
> A book has recently been published at Naples with the object of showing that the doctrine of the motion of the earth and the immobility of the sun is not opposed to the sacred scriptures or to the Catholic faith. This book is in great danger of falling under the suspicion of the Congregation of the Holy Office for the reason I mentioned above, namely that it drags the scriptures into the discussion. I will do my best to obtain a copy for you before anything happens.

The book referred to by Ciàmpoli was called a Letter because supposedly addressed to the General of the Discalced Carmelites and bore the long title *A Letter of the Reverend Father Master Paolo Antonio Foscarini, Carmelite, concerning the opinion of Pythagoras and Copernicus on the motion of the Earth and the immobility of the Sun.* With

[1] A. Favaro, *Le Opere di Galileo Galilei*, vol. xii, pp. 159-60.

this clever but indiscreet book the fat was properly in the fire. Its author appears to have been a man as bouncy and self-confident as Galileo himself, for he came from Naples to Rome to promote the sale of his book by preaching about it and taking on all comers in debate on the subject of the scriptures and Copernicus.

That was surely a provocative action, as Dini and Ciàmpoli had hinted, but Prince Cesi and Father Castelli thought it a marvellous piece of good luck that a distinguished Carmelite priest should have come out so openly in Galileo's favour. Galileo himself to whom Cesi had sent a copy of the book was inspired to fresh ardour in the Copernican cause by its perusal. All three were extremely bad tacticians if they thought Eternal Rome might have its walls breached by such popgun artillery.

Foscarini felt so assured of his cause that he wrote to Cardinal Bellarmine and presented him with a copy of his book. He received the following interesting reply, dated April 12, 1615:

My very reverend Father,

It has been a pleasure to me to read the Italian letter and the Latin paper you sent me. I thank you for both the one and the other and I may tell you that I found them replete with skill and learning. As you ask for my opinion I will give it as briefly as possible because, at the moment, you will have very little time for reading and I have very little time for writing.

First. It seems to me that your Reverence and Signor Galileo would act prudently were you to content yourselves with speaking hypothetically and not absolutely, as I have always believed that Copernicus spoke. To say that on the supposition of the earth's movement and the sun's immobility all the celestial appearances are explained better than by the theory of eccentrics and epicycles, is to speak with excellent good sense and to run no risk whatever. Such a manner of speaking is enough for a mathematician. But to want to affirm that the sun, in very truth, is at the centre of the universe and only rotates on its axis without going from east to west, and that the earth is situated in the third sphere and revolves very swiftly around the sun, is a very dangerous attitude and one calculated not only to annoy all scholastic philosophers and theologians but also to injure our holy faith by contradicting the scriptures. Your Reverence has clearly shown that there are several ways of interpreting the word of God, but you have not applied those methods to any particular passage; and, had you wished to expound by the method of your choice all the texts which you have cited, I feel certain that you would have met with the very greatest difficulties.

Second. As you are aware, the Council of Trent forbids the interpretation of the scriptures in a way contrary to the common opinion of the holy Fathers. Now if your Reverence will read, not merely the Fathers, but modern commentators on Genesis, the Psalms, Ecclesiastes, and Josue, you will discover that all agree in interpreting them literally as teaching that the sun is in the heavens and revolves round the earth with immense speed, and that the earth is very distant from the heavens, at the centre of the universe, and motionless.

Consider, then, in your prudence, whether the Church can tolerate that the scriptures should be interpreted in a manner contrary to that of the holy Fathers and of all modern commentators, both Latin and Greek. It will not do to say that this is not a matter of faith, because though it may not be a matter of faith, *ex parte objecti* or as regards the subject treated, yet it is a matter of faith *ex parte dicentis*, or as regards him who enounces it. Thus he who should deny that Abraham had two sons and Jacob twelve would be just as much a heretic as a man who should deny the virgin birth of Christ, because it is the Holy Spirit who makes known both truths by the mouth of the prophets and apostles.

Third. If there were a real proof that the sun is in the centre of the universe, that the earth is in the third sphere, and that the sun does not go round the earth but the earth round the sun, then we should have to proceed with great circumspection in explaining passages of scripture which appear to teach the contrary, and rather admit that we did not understand them than declare an opinion to be false which is proved to be true. But as for myself, I shall not believe that there are such proofs until they are shown to me. Nor is it a proof that, if the sun be supposed at the centre of the universe and the earth in the third sphere, the celestial appearances are thereby explained, equivalent to a proof that the sun actually is in the centre and the earth in the third sphere. The first kind of proof might, I believe, be found, but as for the second kind, I have the very gravest doubts, and in the case of doubt we ought not to abandon the interpretation of the sacred text as given by the holy Fathers.

I may add that the man who wrote: *The sun rises and sets and returns to its place*, etc., was Solomon, who not only spoke by divine inspiration but was wise and learned, above all others, in human sciences, and in the knowledge of created things. As he had all the wisdom from God himself, it is not likely that he would have made a statement contrary to a truth, either proven or capable of proof. If you tell me that Solomon speaks according to appearances, inasmuch as though the sun seems to us to revolve, it is really the earth that does so, just as when a man is leaving the shore it looks to him as if the shore were receding from the ship, I answer that though it may appear to a voyager as if the shore were receding from the vessel on which he stands rather than the vessel from the shore, yet he knows this to be an illusion and is able to correct it because he sees clearly that it is the ship and not the shore that is in movement. But as to the sun and the earth a wise man has no need to correct his judgment, for his experience tells him plainly that the earth is standing still and that his eyes are not deceived when they report that the sun, moon, and stars are in motion.

With this I salute your paternity affectionately and pray God to grant you all happiness.

From my house, April 12, 1615.

Your very reverend Paternity's brother,

Cardinal Bellarmine[1]

It would obviously be anachronistic and unfair to judge St Robert Bellarmine's views on scripture by the standards of modern Catholic biblical scholarship, especially as developed since the publication of Pope Pius XII's encyclical *Divino Afflante Spiritu* in 1943—curiously the fourth centenary year of the publication of *De Revolutionibus Orbium Coelestium*. The development of Christian doctrine has been a continuous one since the apostolic age, as the implications of divine revelation became clearer to the Church under the guidance of the Holy Spirit, and much is obvious now to the instructed Catholic mind which was far from plain even to so great a man as Bellarmine.

But if it be asked how does the cardinal fare when judged by the scriptural standards of such highly intelligent Catholics of his own time as Galileo himself, as Foscarini, as Castelli, as the Jesuit Pereira, and several others, the answer must surely be not too well. For instance, when he

[1] Favaro, *Le Opere di Galileo Galilei*, vol. xii, pp. 171-2. Bellarmine's belief that Copernicus had spoken only hypothetically was due to Osiander's preface.

9. Pope Urban VIII, 1623–1644.

says that 'the Council of Trent forbids the interpretation of scripture in a way contrary to the common opinion of the Fathers of the Church', Galileo was able to reply with the very words of the conciliar Fathers at the fourth session, held on April 8, 1546: 'So far as I can find,' he wrote in the *Letter to the Grand Duchess Christina*, 'all that is prohibited is the "perverting into senses contrary to that of holy mother Church or that of the unanimous agreement of the Fathers, matters of faith and morals pertaining to the upbuilding [*aedificationem*] of Christian doctrine". But the mobility or stability of the earth or sun is neither a matter of faith nor contrary to morals.'[1] Galileo also cited the Spanish Augustinian, Didacus à Stunica's (Diego de Zuñiga) *Commentary on the Book of Job*, published at Toledo in 1584. This book, which had freely circulated among Catholic students for thirty-one years, most effectively exploded the objection drawn from the unanimous agreement of the Fathers.

The great genius of *The Starry Messenger* shows himself somewhat arrogant and snobbish in the *Letter to the Grand Duchess Christina*. For instance, when trying to explain why the inspired writers of the scriptures speak according to the appearances when, of course, they knew the reality of heliocentrism (which they plainly did not, as it has no bearing on the 'salvation history' that was their only concern), he writes: 'It is sufficiently obvious that to attribute motion to the sun and rest to the earth was necessary lest the shallow minds of the common people

---

[1] Pope Leo XIII cites the same passage from Trent in his encyclical *Providentissimus Deus* on the study of scripture, November 18, 1893.

should become confused, obstinate and contumacious in yielding assent to the principal . . . articles of faith.'[1] It may well be doubted whether the common people, also called the herd, cared two pins what the earth did with itself, provided it afforded them enough sustenance to keep body and soul together at that time of acute economic crisis in Italy. Galileo himself was doubly affected by the crisis, for it kept him poor all his life and it also made the unfortunate Aristotelian professors cling to the traditional teachings on which their bread and dripping depended.

The notorious Caccini, who had constituted himself defender of the faith against the wicked attacks of the Galileans, had gone to Rome against his General's wishes, and there formally denounced Galileo to the Inquisition. The witnesses he produced told quite contradictory stories, and the case was dismissed out of hand. But Caccini was a persistent type of foe and had a large backing of Aristotelians in Rome. This was in 1615. As far back as 1613 Galileo had avowed to Belisario Vinta, the then secretary of the Grand Duke, that 'all his life and being henceforward depended' on bringing the world to accept Copernicanism as a physical truth. He was ill during the winter of 1615 but decided all the same that he must again journey to Rome to fight Caccini to the death. He set out, as Banfi puts it, 'with the heroic blindness of an apostle and the enthusiastic faith of a boy'.[2]

---

[1] Stillman Drake, *Discoveries and Opinions of Galileo*, p. 200.
[2] A. Banfi, *Vita di Galileo Galilei*, p. 148.

The First Brush
with the Inquisition

The First Brush
with the Inquisition

THE Tuscan Ambassador in Rome, Piero Guicciardini, was horrified when he heard that Galileo was coming to the city, and protested vigorously to the new Tuscan secretary of state Curzio Picchena, Vinta's successor:

I am told that Galileo is coming here.... As his views on science and some other matters are not to the taste of the consultors and cardinals of the Holy Office, Bellarmine, among others, has told me that while all respect is due to whatever arrangements have the sanction of his Serene Highness, if Galileo stays here any length of time he is certain to come out with some defence or justification of his opinions.... I do not know whether he has changed those opinions nor whether his temper has improved, but this I know for certain that some Dominicans and others who are very influential with the Holy Office bear him no goodwill. This is not the place to come to dispute about the moon, nor is this the time in which to propound and defend novelties.[1]

But Galileo, who began his campaign immediately after his arrival in Rome, was purring with optimism and told the same Curzio Picchena on December 12 that he found the way clear to maintain and increase his reputation, and felt so pleased with life that his health, recently very bad, 'was improving not a little in consequence'. Dear Galileo, how attractive he can be, and how maddening. He had all the resilience of a high-spirited boy and more than a dash of the same charming creature's irresponsibility. From all accounts, he appears to have taken an unholy delight in baiting and exasperating the opposition. Another of his many priest friends and admirers, Antonio Querengo, said in a letter of January 20, 1616, to Cardinal d'Este at Modena: 'Your Lordship would enjoy Galileo's discourses immensely. . . . He turns the laugh against all his opponents and answers their objections in such a way as to make them look perfectly ridiculous.' Surely not the best way to win friends and influence people!

The Tuscan ambassador's next letter from Rome to the Grand Duke's secretary, Picchena, dated March 4, 1616, sums up the situation as seen by that anxious man:

Galileo sets more store by his own opinion than by the advice of his friends. Cardinal del Monte and myself (though my influence with the man is small), as well as other cardinals of

[1] Letter of December 5, 1615 (Favaro, *Le Opere di Galileo Galilei*, vol xii, pp. 206-7). Galileo arrived in Rome on December 7.

the Holy Office, have endeavoured to pacify him and persuade him not to stir up this affair but, if he wished to hold his opinion, to hold it quietly, without using so much violence in his attempts to force others into holding it. We all doubt very much whether his coming here is not going to prove prejudicial and dangerous for him. As we did not appear to him to be sufficiently enthusiastic about his plans and wishes, after having bothered and tried several cardinals with his story, he concentrated on Cardinal Orsini ... and on Wednesday last Orsini spoke to the pope in a consistory on his behalf. The pope told the cardinal that it would be a good thing if he could persuade Galileo to abandon his opinion. Orsini made some answer or other ... whereupon the pope told him that the question had been referred to the cardinals of the Holy Office. ...

I do not think that there is any possibility of Galileo suffering in person, because as a good and sensible man he will be ready to submit to the decision of the Church. But he gets hotly excited about these views of his, and has an extremely passionate temper, with little patience and prudence to keep it in control. It is this irritability that makes the skies of Rome very dangerous for him.

Cardinal Orsini was the youngest member of the Sacred College, aged twenty-two. Like so many of his generation, he was a strong supporter of Galileo who had well and truly set the stage for his own undoing. The cardinals of the Holy Office submitted two propositions for the verdict of their eleven consultant theologians, many of them highly accomplished in their own discipline but all of them unqualified to judge in matters of physical science and astronomy properly so called.

On the first proposition, that the sun is at the centre of the world and altogether devoid of local motion, they pronounced unanimously that it was foolish and absurd philosophically, and formally heretical as contradicting the doctrine of holy scripture in many places. On the second proposition, that the earth is not the centre of the world but moves as a whole and also with a diurnal motion, meaning that it rotates on its axis, the brave eleven were all agreed that it merited the same censure in philosophy and, from a theological standpoint, was at least erroneous in the faith.

This lamentable report, which was laid before the cardinals of the Holy Office on February 24, 1616, has been the delight of anti-Catholic scoffers ever since. They are entitled to their fun but might remember that it was not a case of religion condemning science, but of bad, outmoded science condemning good science. The cardinals of the Holy Office relegated the report to the files of the Roman Inquisition where it remained gathering dust for seventeen years.

Eleven days later, on March 5, the Congregation issued a decree condemning outright Paolo Foscarini's *Letter*,[1] but only suspending 'until they be corrected' the *Book of the Revolutions* by Copernicus and the *Commentary on the Book of Job* by Didacus à Stunica. The word 'heretical' used by the consultors was omitted from the decree and Galileo's name was not mentioned at all, nor was his openly Copernican *Letters on Sunspots* placed on the Index. But he did not get off scot-free.

By order of the gloomy, authoritarian Paul V, the crusader from Florence was to appear privately before Cardinal

---

[1] Its publisher was arrested and imprisoned at Naples, soon after the issue of the decree. Foscarini himself died the same year.

Bellarmine on February 25, 1616, and be admonished by him to abandon the propositions condemned on the previous day by the theologians, though he could continue to hold and defend them as hypotheses. In case he refused to abandon Copernicanism as physical fact, the Commissary General of the Holy Office was to order him, before a notary and witnesses, 'that he abstain altogether from teaching, defending, or discussing this opinion and doctrine, and that he is to be imprisoned if he remains obstinate'.[1] That document would seem to point plainly to two separate occasions, one at Bellarmine's residence, and a second, in case the Cardinal had to report failure, at the Holy Office headquarters where the Commissary would have his notary and witnesses ready.

But there is another and very strange document in the Vatican files, dated a day later, that is February 26, which has the appearance of a report on what took place the previous day. It runs as follows:

At the palace, the usual residence of the afore-named Lord Cardinal Bellarmine, the said Galileo, having been summoned and standing before his Lordship, was, in the presence of the very Reverend Father Michael Angelo Seghiti de Lauda, of the Order of Preachers, Commissary General of the Holy Office, admonished by the Cardinal of the error of the afore-said opinion and that he should abandon it; and immediately thereafter [*successive ac incontinenti*], in presence of myself, other witnesses, and the Lord Cardinal, who was still in the room, the said Commissary did enjoin upon the said Galileo, there present, and did order him [in his own name], the name of His Holiness the Pope, and the names of all the cardinals

[1] A. Favaro, *Galileo e l'Inquisizione*, p. 61.

105

of the Congregation of the Holy Office, to relinquish altogether the opinion in question, namely that the sun is the centre of the universe and immovable and that the earth moves; nor henceforth to hold, teach, or defend it in any way, either orally or in writing. Otherwise proceedings would be taken against him in the Holy Office. The said Galileo acquiesced in this ruling and promised to obey it.

Done at Rome, in the place aforementioned, in presence of the Reverend Badino Nores from Nicosia in the Kingdom of Cyprus, and Augustino Mongardo, of the diocese of Montepulciano, both witnesses belonging to the said Lord Cardinal's household.

That document is the crux of the whole story of Galileo's condemnation. There has been controversy about it, not even yet ended, ever since, in 1870, the German scholar Emil Wohlwill called attention to the discrepancy between it and a protocol of a meeting of the Holy Office on March 3, 1616, published for the first time that same year, 1870:

Thursday, March 3, 1616.

The Lord Cardinal Bellarmine having reported that Galileo Galilei, the mathematician, had, according to instructions of the Sacred Congregation, been admonished to abandon the opinion he has hitherto held, to the effect that the sun is the centre of the spheres and immovable, and that the earth moves, and had acquiesced therein; and the decree of the Congregation having been registered, by which were suspended and prohibited respectively the writings of Nicholas Copernicus *De revolutionibus orbium coelestium*, of Diego di Zuñiga on the book of Job, and of Paolo Antonio Foscarini, Carmelite Friar—His Holiness ordered this edict of suspension and prohibition respectively, to be published by the master of the sacred palace.[1]

Galileo remained in Rome for three months after the decision of the Holy Office was made known to him by Cardinal Bellarmine. He seems to have been very little depressed at the time by that decision, since he could still discuss Copernicanism with perfect freedom as a hypothesis. He even told friends that he had won a signal victory over his malign and ignorant enemies. One friend, the Venetian diplomat Sagredo, wrote to him in the following terms:

> Now that I have learned from your valued letters the particulars of the spiteful, devilish ... accusations against you, and the issue of them which entirely frustrates the purposes of your ignorant and malicious foes, I, and all the friends to whom I have communicated your letters, are quite set at rest.[2]

As appeared a little later on, the poor fellow was just whistling in the dark, even though he was given a private audience lasting three-quarters of an hour on March 11 by the pope who had condemned him. He described it as a 'benignissima audienza' and wrote with much apparent satisfaction about it to the Tuscan secretary of state, Pichena, the following day:

> I told His Holiness the reason for my coming to Rome ... and made known to him the malice of my persecutors and some of their calumnies against me. He answered that he was well aware of my uprightness and sincerity of mind, and when

---

[1] It appeared originally in an Italian periodical called the *Rivista Europea* and was reprinted in A. Favaro, *Galileo e l'Inquisizione*, p. 16.

[2] Translation from Gebler, *Galileo Galilei and the Roman Curia*, p. 87.

I gave evidence of being still somewhat anxious about the future, owing to my fear of being pursued with implacable hate by my enemies, he consoled me and said that I might put away all care, because I was held in so much esteem both by himself and by the whole congregation of cardinals that they would not lightly lend their ears to calumnious reports. During his life-time, he continued, I might feel quite secure, and before I took my departure he assured me several times that he bore me the greatest goodwill and was ready to show his affection and favour towards me on all occasions.[1]

But the malicious foes continued with their attacks and spread a lying rumour that he had been compelled to recant and given a salutary penance. To stop the mouths of those calumniators, he applied confidently to Cardinal Bellarmine for a statement of what had really happened at his residence on February 25. St Robert readily agreed and issued him the following certificate written in his own hand, which Galileo carefully preserved for the rest of his life:

We, Robert, Cardinal Bellarmine, having heard that Signor Galileo Galilei has been calumniously reported to have abjured in our hand, and moreover to have been punished with a salutary penance, and having been asked to make known the truth as to this, declare that the said Signor Galileo has not abjured in our hand, nor in the hand of anybody else here in Rome, nor, so far as we are aware, in any place whatever, any opinion or doctrine held by him: neither has any penance, salutary or otherwise, been imposed upon him. All that happened was this. The declaration made by the Holy Father and published by the Sacred Congregation of the Index was intimated to him, wherein it is declared that the doctrine attributed to Copernicus that the earth moves round the sun

[1] Favaro, *Le Opere di Galileo Galilei*, vol. xii, pp. 247-9.

and that the sun is in the centre of the universe and does not move from east to west, is contrary to the holy scriptures, and therefore cannot be defended nor held.

In witness whereof we have written and subscribed these presents with our own hand the 26th day of May, 1616.

As above, Robert Cardinal Bellarmine.[1]

That certificate, Galileo's own confident attitude and the protocol of the Holy Office issued on March 3, 1616, form a powerful combined proof that the great scientist was at no time called before the Commissary General and forbidden absolutely to hold, teach or defend in any way, either orally or in writing, the theory of Copernicus.

[1] A. Favaro, *Galileo e l'Inquisizione*, p. 68.

The Wrangler

The Wrangler

JUNE is no month for any sensible person to stay in Rome, except by dire necessity. But Galileo would have stayed, had he not been ordered back to Florence by the Grand Duke who was anxious to keep him out of any further mischief. He returned bitterly aggrieved that he had failed to convert the world generally by the persuasiveness of his tongue. A friend told him that he had 'a way of bewitching people', but the spell had not worked in the end. He remained out of circulation for two years after his return home, being mostly unwell.

However, he was not a man to accept defeat without a struggle. Precluded from presenting his views openly, he began in 1618 to look round for some way of propagating them indirectly. Thus he re-wrote a paper which he had composed two years before in Rome dealing with the phenomenon of the tides. Kepler had correctly associated the tides with the moon, but Galileo was strongly opposed to mysterious forces acting at a distance. He wanted mechanical explanations and so sponsored a theory that the tides were the result of the combined axial and orbital movements of the earth. The tides, in fact, proved the earth to be in motion. This he presented to the youthful Cardinal Orsini as physical evidence for the truth of Copernicanism. Mr Stillman Drake has shown that the theory is by no means as silly as people such as Arthur Koestler are inclined to regard it. 'In place of criticizing either Kepler or Galileo, one might well say that both were correct in their physical intuitions, the one seeking an explanatory motion of the earth and the other seeking an explanatory attraction of the moon.'[1]

Though Newton's theory of gravitation was to decide in favour of Kepler rather than Galileo, the latter's theory of the tides held its own for a hundred years. He cherished it greatly and used it as his principal physical argument in his fatal *Dialogue on the Two Great World Systems*, published in 1632. In 1618 he added to his thesis a preface describing it as merely an ingenious speculation and dispatched it to the Archduke Leopold of Austria, hoping, perhaps, that that influential gentleman would publish it for him, and thus relieve him of any responsibility. The Archduke did not bite, but three comets which appeared in rapid succession during the autumn of 1618, the years marking the opening phases of the terrible Thirty Years War, afforded Galileo a safer if less direct approach to his problem

[1] *Origin and Fate of Galileo's Theory of the Tides.* Extracted from *Physis*, vol. II—Fasc. 3—1961, Florence, pp. 85-93.

of how to carry on his own war for Copernicus. At this time he was confined to bed by illness and so could not study the comets himself, but his friends did and conveyed to him their findings. Ancient writers had regarded comets as meteorological appearances, sort of will-o'-the-wisps, and not properly heavenly bodies at all. But Tycho Brahe proved observationally that the comet of 1577 was located far beyond the moon, and in his *Letters on Sunspots* Galileo had endorsed this view.

When the Jesuit Orazio Grassi published a lecture he had given on the comets and more or less implied that they were an insuperable argument against heliocentrism, Galileo's rage knew no bounds. The Jesuits, whom he had once thought to be his friends, had done little to help him in 1616, and now, with Grassi's effusion, they showed themselves to be the allies of the unspeakable Caccini. The sad fact is that the Jesuit scientists were under orders from their General, Claudio Acquaviva, to stand by Aristotle, though their best men such as Clavius and Grienberger certainly leaned towards Copernicanism in their hearts.

Galileo's jottings in the margins of Grassi's lecture would, in Professor de Santillana's opinion, 'make a vocabulary of good Tuscan abuse'. Here are a few of the expletives used: unmannerly poltroon, swindler, ungrateful boor, shameless creature, rude ruffian. The Professor, taking a cue from his hero, added a few choice specimens of his own: 'So these trained seals who had kept to their holes in time of crisis were now gloating about him and oraculating again. . . .'[1]

[1] *The Crime of Galileo*, Chicago, 1955, p. 152.

Galileo's good friend, Mario Guiducci, offered to write an answer to Grassi or to put his name to an answer written by the scientist himself. The *Discourse on the Comets* appeared in June, 1619. The hand might be the hand of Esau but the voice was unquestionably the voice of Jacob. Galileo's old friend Maffeo Barberini wrote a Latin poem to honour the return of the great man to the lists and there was general rejoicing that so matchless a prose writer had conquered his hard fate and begun again to contribute to the gaiety of nations. Grassi was not a complete fool, for he had drawn up the plans for the great church of San Ignacio in Rome. But on this occasion he proved that he could be downright silly. He must have known how deadly dangerous Galileo could be in argument, and yet he went out of his way to provoke him in a retort to the Guiducci book, in a work which he entitled *The Astronomical and Philosophical Balance.*

Masquerading as one of his own pupils, he wrote under the name of Lothario Sarsi and, brushing Guiducci aside, wrote a venomous and slashing attack on Galileo himself. He fairly asked to be slaughtered and Galileo, taking plenty of time, obliged. The answer did not appear until 1623, three years after the attack. It was called *The Assayer—Il Saggiatore*—the crude steelyard of Sarsi being replaced by the delicate instrument which is employed in the assay of pure gold. 'The result was the greatest polemic ever written in physical science' (Stillman Drake). The slaughter of Sarsi was merely incidental; Galileo just laughed the man off the stage.

In the midst of many irrelevancies and extremely witty, though often unfair, sallies at Sarsi's expense, there occur other passages which are classical statements of scientific reasoning and the experimental method, of the duty to be sceptical about quoting authorities, and of not treating Aristotle as though he alone had been given eyes to see for all the generations of mankind. In *The Assayer*, too, is to be found the distinction, perfectly illustrated, between the primary and secondary qualities of material things. It was a truly epoch-making book, a very great scientist's scientific manifesto.

Galileo had an enormous piece of good fortune in the publication of his book, for it coincided with the election to the papacy of his old friend and admirer, Maffeo Barberini, as Pope Urban VIII, and he was able to dedicate *The Assayer* to him. The pope thoroughly enjoyed the book and, when its author came to Rome where it was published, in the spring of 1624, accorded him six long audiences in the space of six weeks, gave him a pension for his son Vincenzo, a valuable work of art, and gold and silver medals. In a testimonial to the court of the Medici, then ruled by the Grand Duchess Christina as Cosimo II had died and her other son Ferdinand was a minor, Pope Urban extolled the virtues and piety of this 'great man whose fame shines in the heavens and goes far and wide on earth'. But much appreciated as he undoubtedly was, Galileo could not persuade the pope to rescind the decree of 1616. Urban pointed out to him that Copernicanism had not been con-

demned as heretical but only, in the then state of knowledge, as risky (*temeraria*). Galileo certainly gathered from
the pope that he could say what he pleased in support of
Copernicus, provided that he kept clear of theological and
scriptural arguments, and spoke hypothetically. This is addi-
tional proof that he was never given the Commissary of
the Inquisition's strict injunction.

After this fourth visit to Rome, Galileo returned to
Florence in a much happier frame of mind. His daughter,
the incomparable nun Suor Maria Celeste, had begun to
play an increasingly important part in his life. He had
treated her rather heartlessly by immuring her in a convent
at Arcetri near Florence when she was only a young girl.
As we have seen, the convent was very poor and she and
her sister Livia had suffered dire privations. Livia became
a permanent invalid in consequence, but her elder, Virginia,
in religion Suor Maria Celeste, wove her sufferings into
the loveliest of garlands and showed a complete forgiveness
and boundless generosity and love for her indifferent father.

Her letters to him appear to date from 1623, the year of
The Assayer, and excellent English versions of them are
to be found in an anonymous book published in London
in 1870, under the title: *The Private Life of Galileo through
the Letters of Sister Maria Celeste*. The author is known to
have been Mary Allan Olney. Maria Celeste had won her
father round completely by the year 1623. Extracts from a
few of the letters written that year may let a little of the
air of heaven into these disputes and intrigues of earth.

Shirts, letters, dinner napkins

I send back the rest of your shirts which we have been working on, also the apron which I have mended as well as I possibly could. I likewise return the letters you sent me to read; they are so beautiful that my desire to see more of them is greatly increased. I cannot begin working on the dinner napkins until you send the pieces to add on. Please bear in mind that the said pieces must be long, owing to the dinner napkins being a trifle short.

On the accession of Urban VIII

I imagine that by this time you will have written a most beautiful letter to congratulate him on his having obtained the tiara. As I feel rather curious about it I should like extremely, if you do not object, to see a copy of what you may have written. I thank you infinitely for what you have sent, and also for the melons, which we were very glad to get. As I have written in very great haste, I must beg you to excuse the bad handwriting. All join me in hearty greeting.

Father explains and daughter is abashed

From your beloved letter I see fully how little knowledge of the world I must possess to have thought as I did that you would write immediately to such a personage, to one who is in fact the head of Christendom. I therefore thank you for the hint you have given me, and feel sure that your love for me will induce you to excuse my ignorance as well as many other faults which I possess. I trust that, always being warned and reproved by you, I may gain in knowledge and discretion ... I put by carefully the letters you write me daily, and when not engaged with my duties I read them over and over again. This is the greatest pleasure I have.

Father's letters and daughter's love

I leave you to imagine how pleased I am to read the letters you constantly send me. . . . Nevertheless, I feel it is a little hard to hear that you intend leaving home so soon, because I shall have to do without you and for a long time, too, if am not mistaken. And your Lordship may believe that I am speaking the truth when I say that except you there is not a creature who gives me any comfort. But I will not grieve at your departure because of this, for that would be to complain when you had cause for rejoicing. Therefore I too will rejoice and continue to pray God to give you grace and health to make a prosperous journey.

Bed-hangings and cakes

As I have no sleeping room of my own, Sister Diamanta kindly allows me to share hers, depriving herself of the company of her own sister for my sake. But the room is so bitterly cold, that with my head in the state in which it is at present, I do not know how I shall remain, unless you can help me by lending me a set of those white bed-hangings which you will not want now. Moreover, I beg you to be so kind as to send me that book of yours which has just been published, [Il Saggiatore], so that I may read it for I have a great desire to see it.

These few cakes I send are some I made a few days ago, intending to give them to you when you came to bid us adieu. As your departure is not so near as we feared I send them lest they should get dry.

Galileo began the writing of his splendid but fatal book in 1625, entitling it, *Dialogue Concerning the Two Great World Systems—Ptolemaic and Copernican*. He went about the work in leisurely fashion and teased his friends who were longing to read it by dropping it altogether for months at a time. This dallying was due principally to wretched health, an impediment he overcame by sheer power of will and character. In 1628 he became so ill that his life was despaired of. But he resumed composition of the *Dialogue* the following year and completed it triumphantly in January, 1630. It was a very considerable work, running to 500 manuscript pages.

In the *Dialogue*, handled with brilliant literary ability, Galileo by means of the two characters, his friends Sagredo and Salviati, both then dead, defended Copernicanism openly as established physical truth, using as his principal argument his questionable theory of the tides. His third character, Simplicio, is a genial anti-Copernican and is made the mouthpiece of an argument against heliocentrism excogitated and presented to Galileo by no less a person than Pope Urban himself. He did not by this intend in the least to make game of the pope, but Urban, who soon had it pointed out to him by Galileo's enemies, chose to regard it as a personal insult and became extremely embittered against his former friend.

In May, 1630, Galileo arrived in Rome with his manuscript, seeking licence to print. The new Grand Duke of Tuscany, Ferdinand II, lent him his own litter and bearers for the two-hundred mile journey, and he was to be the guest of the new Tuscan ambassador, a warm admirer and friend named Francesco Niccolini, at the Villa Medici. Everything seemed to smile on him at first. Even the pope, not yet aware of the way his argument had been used, proved genial and personally gave the master of the sacred palace, Niccolò Riccardi, O.P., general directions about the censorship of the book.

Riccardi, affectionately known as the 'Monster' on account of his huge girth, was a very charming and popular

121

man. Though like Galileo a Florentine and so most favourably disposed, he did not relish dealing with a book about astronomy, but reading in the preface that the author filially submitted himself in all things to Holy Mother Church and her decrees, observing the interest of the pope and the lively expectation of the Tuscan Ambassador, and also the general expectation in cultured circles, he became easier in mind and handed over the manuscript for scientific and mathematical revision to Padre Raffaello Visconti, who found very little wrong with it and gave his assent to publication. So did Riccardi, but still with a few provisos. Galileo was on top of the world for the moment and made arrangements with his good friends Prince Cesi and Ciàmpoli, then in the strong position of private secretary to Pope Urban, for publication of the book in Rome.

The great man had not been many weeks back in Florence when his good luck began to fade. First came the grievous news that Prince Cesi was dead, an irreparable blow. Then in August Castelli wrote to him urging that for 'many most weighty reasons which he did not wish to commit to paper', he should have the book printed in Florence and as soon as possible. To reinforce Castelli's pleas the plague descended on Central Italy, making communications between Rome and Florence impossible.

Here, momentarily to sweeten the bitter record, is an extract from a letter of Suor Maria Celeste to her father, who had meantime bought a small country house adjoining the Convent at Arcetri, so as to be near his daughters:

I send you two pots of electuary as a preservative against the plague. The one without the label consists of dried figs, walnuts, rue and salt, mixed together with honey. A piece the size of a walnut is to be taken in the morning, fasting, with a little Greek wine (or any other good wine). They say its efficacy is wonderful. It is true that what is in the pot is baked rather too much; we did not take into account the tendency the figs have to get into lumps. The other pot is to be taken in the same way; the taste is rather more tart. If you like to continue taking either of them, we will try to make it better next time.

This dear, heroic nun regretted her difficult cloistered life only in one respect: 'It prevents me from attending on you personally. My thoughts are always with you and I long to have news of you daily.' When her brother Vincenzo's fiancée visited the convent she and her sister were delighted with her charm of manner and beauty; 'but what gave me the greatest joy was to see that she is fond of you, since from that we may judge that she will not be wanting in such loving attention and duty as it would be our delight to render you were it permitted'.[1]

Cut off from Rome, Galileo was dependent on his friend Ambassador Niccolini, or rather on Niccolini's wife Caterina, who was the 'Monster's' very loving cousin. She easily wheedled him into granting permission for the final revision and printing of the *Dialogue* to be done in Florence, but he obstinately held on to the Preface and conclusion of the book which he wanted to arrange in accordance with the pope's wishes.

[1] Translation from Mary Allan Olney, *The Private Life of Galileo*, London, 1870.

Why was it necessary to have the work done in Florence when Ciàmpoli with all his influence was still available and eager in Rome? 'From Castelli's dark allusions,' writes Professor de Santillana, 'it is easy to infer that the Jesuits, advised by Grassi and Scheiner, had swung into action'.[1] What universal mischief makers those Jesuits were! At that very time their missionaries in China were teaching the mandarins the Copernican views as established by the great Galileo. It is strange that Castelli's dark allusions have not the backing up of a single scrap of documentary evidence.

Riccardi held out against all inducements until July 19, 1631, when at long last, and as it were 'dragged by the hair', in Niccolini's phrase, he handed over to the Embassy at the Villa Medici the Preface and Conclusion of the *Dialogue*. Six months later, in February, 1632, Galileo was able proudly to present the first printed copy of the book, which had caused him so much vexation and was to bring about his destruction, to his sovereign the Grand Duke Ferdinand.

[1] *The Crime of Galileo*, p. 185.

Eclipse

Eclipse

NOT even the most ardent admirer of Galileo, and I count
myself such, can deny that he resorted to very shifty prac-
tices to obtain an *imprimatur* for his *Dialogue*. Through a
cabal of his friends in Rome he extorted from the very
genial and friendly master of the sacred palace a very
reluctant permission to have the work printed and censored
in Florence, where by other underhand manoeuvres he
secured a censor entirely of his own mind. Riccardi protested in vain, and was eventually cajoled and browbeaten
into letting his *imprimatur* appear on the book. Poor, portly
Riccardi, a lovable, conscientious man, got into serious
trouble, and it is not too easy to forgive Galileo for causing
it. True, he passionately longed to get the truth across,
but even in so good a cause not all means are justifiable. It
did not take the pope and the Holy Office officials very

long to discover that they had been completely outwitted. Urban VIII was a very proud prelate. To have been insulted and hoodwinked by a man he had admired and greatly honoured threw him into an understandable rage.

The *Dialogue* was greeted with enthusiastic applause by Galileo's friends when published in February, 1632. The deadly quality of its irony may be judged by the following brief extract from the mouth of Simplicio:

> Oh, to whom must we betake ourselves if Aristotle be removed from the chair? What other author have we to follow in our schools, our studies and academies? What philosopher has written on all the parts of natural philosophy, and so methodically as not to have overlooked a single conclusion? Must we then destroy this asylum, this Prytaneum wherein so many students have found a convenient resting place, where without being exposed to the injuries of the weather one may acquire an intimate knowledge of nature, merely by turning over a few leaves.[1]

In March of that year, 1632, the Spanish ambassador, Cardinal Borgia, accused the pope to his face in a sonsistory of supporting the heretics in the war then raging. So Urban did, by his backing Richelieu and the Protestant Gustavus Adolphus against the Habsburg Emperor, Ferdinand II, head of the Catholic league. Urban might have killed Borgia but for his diplomatic immunity. He shut himself up in his newly built summer residence of Castel Gandolfo and there indulged in the blackest thoughts of revenge on Spain, and on the two men who had insulted him, Galileo and Borgia. He would show them whether he supported Protestants by

[1] Translation from John Elliot Drinkwater (— Bethune), *The Life of Galileo Galilei*, op. cit., p. 55f.

GALILEO GALILEI LINCEO FILOSOFO E MATEMATICO DEL SER^mo GRAN DVCA DI TOSC... GALILEO

Villamœna Feat

10. Frontispiece of *Il Saggiatore*, 1623, showing a portrait of Galileo.

11. Ferdinand II de' Medici, 1610–1670. *From a painting by Giusto Sustermans.*

exacting stern reparation from a bad Catholic who taught pernicious theories and defied the edicts of the holy see.

In August, six months after its appearance, the publisher Landine was ordered peremptorily, from Rome, to suspend sales of the *Dialogue*. On October 1 Galileo was summoned before the Inquisitor in Florence, and in the presence of a notary and witnesses strictly ordered to appear before the Commissary General of the Inquisition in Rome within the space of one month. This order came as a terrible shock to him. He fell seriously ill and appealed to the Grand Duke to plead that he might be questioned in Florence and spared the winter journey to Rome. But Ferdinand was himself afraid of spiritual bolts from the Vatican and rather timidly kept out of the mess, though his heart still leaned to Galileo. The most that the poor stricken genius could obtain from the heartless bureaucrats of the Vatican was a postponement to the end of December when, if he did not appear, he would be brought to Rome forcibly and in chains. He obtained a certificate signed by three doctors testifying that his pulse was irregular, that he suffered from grave weakness of the stomach and persistent insomnia, that they had also observed a serious hernia with rupture of the peritoneum. 'If in the least aggravated, all these symptoms might become dangerous to life.' Eventually the Grand Duke advised him to go, and as before, put at his service his own litter and bearers. After twenty-three painful days on the road, he reached the Tuscan Embassy and met with a loving reception from Caterina Niccolini, 'queen of all kindness', as he called her. That was on February 13, 1633.

The fact that he had obeyed the summons to Rome is itself very remarkable. He could so easily have slipped into Switzerland or some other place where the pope's writ did not run. He was, in fact, warmly invited back to Venetian territory, where he would have been perfectly safe, by friends who had forgiven his ingratitude in leaving it twenty-two years before. He refused to take any of those ways out, partly because of his strong Catholic faith and partly also because he felt in his pride capable of defeating the Inquisition. When told that the authorities had discovered in the Vatican files a document proving that he had been given an absolute injunction by the Commissary General in 1616, he saw nothing very sinister in the occurrence, for he had Bellarmine's certificate in the cardinal's own hand to discredit the story. As the days went by, however, he became more and more dejected. Father Castelli, his dearest friend, had been purposely sent away from Rome, and Niccolini, now his only standby, advised him in desperation not to argue with the inquisitors, but to give way and agree to anything they demanded of him.

The illustrious defendant was obliged at last to leave the Villa Medici and surrender formally to the Inquisition. But he was not, as usual in such cases, put in the common prison of the Holy Office. He was by special privilege assigned a comfortable suite of rooms, usually occupied by high functionaries of the Inquisition, in the Holy Office headquarters. These are situated alongside the Dominican church of Santa Maria Sopra Minerva and close to the Pantheon or St Mary of the Martyrs, which Urban VIII had rifled of its lead and bronze. Writing to his friend Geri Bocchineri on April 16, 1633, Galileo reported:

> Contrary to custom, three large and comfortable rooms have been assigned to me, part of the residence of the fiscal of the Holy Office, with free permission to walk about in the spacious apartments. My health is good for which, next to God, I have to thank the great care of the ambassador and his wife, who have a watchful eye for all comforts and far more than I require.

Meanwhile, on April 12, Galileo was interrogated for the first time by the Dominican Commissary of the Inquisition, Fra Vincenzo Maculano da Firenzuola. The transcript of the interrogation was as follows:

Galileo: Respecting the controversy which had arisen on the aforesaid opinion that the sun is stationary and the earth moves, it was decided by the Holy Congregation of the Index that such an opinion, considered as an established fact, contradicted holy scripture and was only admissible as a conjecture, as it was held by Copernicus.

Maculano: Was this decision then communicated to you, and by whom?

Gal: The decision of the Holy Congregation of the Index was made known to me by Cardinal Bellarmine.

Mac: You must state what his Eminence Cardinal Bellarmine told you about the aforesaid decision, and whether he said anything else on the subject and what?

Gal: Signor Cardinal Bellarmine signified to me that the aforesaid opinion of Copernicus might be held as a conjecture, as it had been held by Copernicus, and his Eminence was aware that like Copernicus, I only held that opinion as a conjecture, which is evident from an answer of the same Signor Cardinal to a letter of Father Paolo Antonio

131

Foscarini, provincial of the Carmelites, of which I have a copy, and in which these words occur: 'It appears to me that your reverence and Signor Galileo act wisely in contenting yourselves with speaking *ex suppositione* and not with certainty.' This letter of the cardinal's is dated 12 April, 1615. It means, in other words that that opinion, taken absolutely, must not either be held or defended.

(Galileo was asked to state the decree of February, 1616)

Gal: In the month of February, 1616, Signor Cardinal Bellarmine told me that as the opinion of Copernicus, if adopted absolutely was contrary to holy scripture, it must be neither held nor defended but that it might be held hypothetically and written about in this sense. In accordance with this I possess a certificate of the said Signor Cardinal Bellarmine, given on 26 May, 1616, in which he says that the Copernican opinion may neither be held nor defended, as it is opposed to holy scripture; of which certificate I hereby submit a copy.

Mac: When the above communication was made to you, were any other persons present, and who?

Gal: When Signor Cardinal Bellarmine made known to me what I have reported about Copernican views, some Dominican fathers were present but I did not know them and have never seen them since.

Mac: Was any other command communicated to you on this subject, in the presence of those fathers, by them or anyone else, and what?

Gal: I remember that the transaction took place as follows: Signor Cardinal Bellarmine sent for me one morning and told me certain particulars which I was to bring to the ears of His Holiness before I communicated them to others. But the end of it was that he told me that the Copernican opinion, being contrary to holy scripture, must not be held or defended. It has escaped my memory whether those Dominican fathers were present before, or whether they came afterwards; neither do I remember whether they were present when the Signor Cardinal told me that the said opinion was not to be held. It may be that a command was issued to me that I should not hold nor defend the opinion in question, but I do not remember it for it is several years ago.

Mac: If what was said then, and enjoined on you as a command, were read aloud to you, would you remember it?

Gal: I do not remember that anything else was said or enjoined upon me, nor do I know that I should remember what was said to me, even if it were read to me. I say freely what I do remember, because I do not think I have in any way disobeyed the injunction, that is, have not by any means held nor defended the said opinion that the earth moves and the sun is stationary.

(The Inquisitor reads the command 'that he must neither hold, defend *nor teach that opinion in any way whatsoever*')

Gal: I do not remember that the command was intimated to me by anybody but the Cardinal verbally; and I remember that the command was not to hold or defend. It may be that 'and not to teach' was also there. I do not remember it, neither the definition 'in any way whatsoever', but it may be that it was; for I thought no more about it, nor took any pains to impress the words on my memory, as a few months later I received the certificate now produced, of the said Signor Cardinal Bellarmine of 26 May, in which the injunction given me not to hold nor defend that opinion, is expressly to be found. The other two definitions of the said injunction which have just been made known to me, namely *not to teach* and *in any way*, I have not retained in my memory, I suppose because they are not mentioned in the said certificate, on which I rely and which I have kept as a reminder.

(Galileo is asked if, when he applied for the *imprimatur* for the *Dialogue* he said anything about the Holy Office's command)

Gal: I did not say anything about that command to the master of the palace when I asked for the *imprimatur* for the book, for I did not think it necessary to say anything because I had no scruples about it; for I have neither maintained nor defended the opinion that the earth moves and the sun is stationary in that book, but have rather demonstrated the opposite of the Copernican opinion, and shown that the arguments of Copernicus are weak and not conclusive.[1]

As a consequence of his interrogation, Galileo fell seriously ill and had to go to bed. One shaft of sunlight penetrated his melancholy and pain, a letter from that beloved nun, his daughter Maria Celeste, who causes the honest Marxist Professor Banfi to become lyrical every time he mentions her name. She wrote on April 20:

I have just been informed by Signor Geni of your being imprisoned by the Holy Office. . . . I hope for a prosperous ending with the help of almighty God, to whom I cry without ceasing, recommending you to his care with the greatest love and confidence. . . . Perhaps even while I am writing the crisis may be past and you may be relieved of all anxiety. May it be the Lord's will in whose keeping I leave you.

[1] Translation from Karl von Gebler, *Galileo Galilei and the Roman Curia*, pp. 202-5. Mr Stillman Drake has worked out brilliantly a reconstruction of what may have taken place that day in 1616 at Cardinal Bellarmine's residence. According to it the Dominicans forced themselves on his Lordship who whispered to Galileo to pay no attention to them or to anything they said. It is a highly plausible theory and would account very well for the presence of the 'absolute injunction' in the Vatican files. Mr Drake hopes to publish a full account of his reconstruction at a later date.

She tried to make him forget his grievous anxieties by telling him of all the happenings at Arcetri, the new plantings in his garden, how the vines of whose culture he is such a proud master are thriving, of his falcon, sad at his absence, and about his mule which would not allow anybody but its own true master on its back, and which gave poor Geppo such a toss when he tried to mount, though without injuring him.

Five days after Galileo's first interrogation, on April 17, the three experts appointed to examine the *Dialogue* handed in their report. By a long list of citations they proved conclusively that he had not only discussed the Copernican theory as a hypothesis, as he was entitled to do, but that he had taught, defended and held it proved as physical fact, and had referred to those who differed from him as 'dumb idiots' and 'mental pygmies, hardly deserving to be called human'. Yet the unhappy defendant persisted in saying that in the *Dialogue* he had shown the falsity of Copernicanism which he had renounced in 1616 and never subsequently believed in. As he was under oath to speak the truth, the cardinals of the Holy Office could fairly have charged him with perjury at that point and so have completely broken him. But they did not want to break him and so commissioned Maculano to see him again and endeavour to argue him out of his folly. In a letter to Cardinal Francesco Barberini, the pope's nephew and counsellor who was one of the judges at the trial, and in a restricted measure friendly to the accused, Maculano was happy to report on April 28 that he had been successful:

135

'After many and many arguments and rejoinders had passed between us, by God's grace I obtained my object. He clearly recognized that he had gone too far and erred in his book, and he was ready to make this confession before his judges.'

It makes one's blood boil, even at this distance of time, to think of those wretched judges and that proud, rancorous pope, harrying and browbeating one of the brightest spirits in human history, till broken in health and terrorized, he even offered to add new chapters to his *Dialogue* in refutation of the Copernican views too freely expressed in it, 'through a vainglorious ambition and complacency in desiring to appear more subtle than the generality of popular writers'. Alas! poor Galileo, where be your gibes now, your flashes of merriment, that were wont to set the table on a roar? The confession was in the following revealing terms:

In the course of some days' continuous and attentive reflection on the interrogations put to me on the 16th of the present month, and in particular as to whether, sixteen years ago, an injunction was intimated to me by order of the Holy Office forbidding me to hold, defend or teach 'in any manner' the opinion that had just been condemned—of the motion of the earth and the stability of the sun—it occurred to me to re-peruse my printed *Dialogue* which for three years I had not seen, in order carefully to note whether, contrary to my most sincere intention, there had by inadvertence fallen from my pen anything from which a reader or the authorities might induce the belief that I had contravened the orders of Holy Church. And, being, by the kind permission of the authorities, at liberty to send about my servant, I succeeded in procuring a copy of the book, and having procured it I applied myself with the utmost diligence to its perusal and to a most minute consideration thereof. And as, owing to my not having seen it for so long, it presented itself to me, as it were, like a new writing and by another author, I freely confess that in several places it seemed to me set forth in such a form that a reader ignorant of my real purpose might have had reason to suppose that the arguments adduced on the false side, and which it was my intention to confute, were so expressed as to be calculated to compel conviction by their cogency rather than be easy of solution. Two arguments there are in particular—the one taken from the solar spots, the other from the ebb and flow of the tide—which in truth come to the ear of the reader with far greater show of force and power than ought to have been imparted to them by one who regarded them as inconclusive, and who intended to refute them as indeed I truly and sincerely held and do hold them to be inconclusive and admitting of refutation. And, as an excuse to myself for having fallen into error so foreign to my intention—not contenting myself, I say, with this excuse—I resorted to that of the natural complacency which every man feels with regard to his own subtleties and in showing himself more skilful than the generality of men in devising, even in favour of false propositions, ingenious and plausible arguments. With all this, although with Cicero 'avidior sim gloriae quam satis est', if I had now to set forth the same reasonings without doubt I should so weaken them that they should not be able to make an apparent show of that force of which they are really and essentially devoid. My error, then, has been—and I confess it—one of vainglorious ambition, and of pure ignorance and inadvertence.

This is what occurs to me to say with reference to this particular and which suggested itself to me during the re-perusal of my book.[1]

[1]Translation, Karl von Gerbler, *Galileo Galilei and the Roman Curia*, pp. 214-5.

The proud, implacable pope who had squandered the Church's wealth, the patrimony of the poor, on his wretched grasping nephews, and in spite of the classical scholarship which he affected plundered the monuments of antiquity to serve his own vainglorious purposes, thus giving rise to the Roman gibe 'what the barbarians did not do, the Barberini did', gave vent to his spite against fate and his consciousness of disastrous failure by ordering that a very harsh decree against Galileo be entered in the official acts of the trial. He was to be questioned under threat of torture (incidentally illegal because Galileo was over seventy) as to his intentions in writing his book. If he maintained his views he was to be called upon to recant before a plenary session of the Holy Office; to be condemned to perpetual prison; and strictly enjoined never again to deal orally or in writing with the Copernican question. The *Dialogue* was to be prohibited, and that these ordinances might be generally known, copies of the sentence were to be despatched to all apostolic nuncios and inquisitors, with particular mention of the inquisitor of Florence who must read it in full assembly, and in presence of all the local professors of mathematics.

The only people to whom that decree gave satisfaction were the die-hard Aristotelians and Caccini's clique of intriguers. More thoughtful men, deeply concerned for the welfare of the Church, were appalled by it. With peace and deepest respect to my good friend Professor de Santillana who writes such magnificent tingling prose, they included the Jesuit scientists with the possible exception of Orazio Grassi. Poor fellow, he had his own wounds to lick.

It can be said of Pope Urban, of whom so little good can be said,[1] that he still retained a certain tenderness for Galileo personally, though it was not to be relied on. Two days after the issue of his decree, he assured the Tuscan ambassador that, though the scientist had to be shown the error of his ways, he would see to it that he 'suffered as little distress as possible', and Urban was as good as his word.

Galileo was summoned for his third and final examination on June 21, and questioned under oath about his real convictions on the systems of Ptolemy and Copernicus. He answered that after the Decree of 1616 he had always held as indisputable the position of Ptolemy, that is, the stability of the earth. Three times over he was adjured to speak his real mind, as he had shown it in his *Dialogue*. With the third adjuration torture was mentioned, but he still maintained that ever since 1616 he had rejected Copernicanism as an untrue theory of the heavens.

The whole hearing was a pure formality, as was the threat of torture, and Galileo knew it. He lied obstinately and his judges knew perfectly well that he was lying and perjuring himself, but they took no action of any kind on this count. He was escorted back to his rooms and the following day, June 22, his sentence was read to him. This

[1] His political record is uniformly black, a matter of disastrous diplomacy abroad, and at home of petty aggressions, such as the case of the Duchy of Castro, when he thought he could get away with them. By the end of his long reign the prestige of the papacy had sunk almost to vanishing point among the nations. Religiously, however, he enacted valuable legislation on the beatification and canonization of saints and above all he founded the College of Propaganda, called after him the Urbanum to this day.

took place in the great hall of the Inquisition, on the second floor of the Dominican Convent adjoining the Minerva, where, just opposite, Bernini's engaging little elephant has been so long and patiently carrying the Egyptian obelisk. The cardinals of the Holy Office were present in force, but not the pope, who also did not sign nor ratify the sentence. Galileo was solemnly to abjure the Copernican opinion, to be imprisoned at the pleasure of the Holy Office, and to recite once a week the seven penitential psalms for the following three years. Then he was handed the formula of abjuration and required to recite it on his knees. He did as he was told very abjectly. The formula ran as follows:

I, Galileo Galilei, son of the late Vincenzo Galilei, Florentine, aged seventy years, arraigned personally before this tribunal and kneeling before you ... swear that I have always believed, do now believe and by God's help will for the future believe, all that is held, preached and taught by the holy Catholic and apostolic Roman Church. But whereas ... after an injunction had been judicially intimated to me by this Holy Office, to the effect that I must altogether abandon the false opinion that the sun is the centre of the world and immovable, and that the earth is not the centre of the world and moves, and that I must not hold, defend or teach in any way whatsoever, verbally or in writing, the said doctrine, and after it had been notified to me that the said doctrine was contrary to holy scripture.... I wrote and printed a book in which I discuss this doctrine already condemned, and adduce arguments of great cogency in its favour, without presenting any solution of these; and for this cause I have been pronounced by the Holy Office to be vehemently suspected of heresy, that is to say, of having held and believed that the sun is the centre

140

of the world and immovable, and that the earth is not the centre and moves.

Therefore desiring to remove from the minds of your Eminences, and of all faithful Christians, this strong suspicion, reasonably conceived against me, with sincere heart and unfeigned faith, I abjure, curse and detest the aforesaid errors and heresies, and generally every other error and sect whatsoever contrary to the said holy Church; and I swear that in future I will never again say or assert, verbally or in writing, anything that might furnish occasion for a similar suspicion regarding me; but that should I know any heretic or person suspected of heresy, I will denounce him to this Holy Office, or to the Inquisitor and Ordinary of the place where I may be. Further I swear and promise to fulfil and observe in their integrity all penances that have been or that shall be imposed upon me by this Holy Office.... So help me God and these his holy gospels which I touch with my hand.

I, Galileo Galilei, have abjured, sworn, promised and bound myself as above; and in witness of the truth thereof I have with my own hand subscribed the present document of my abjuration and recited it word for word at Rome, in the Convent of the Minerva, this 22nd day of June, 1633.[1]

That was the end of the whole miserable business. Two days later Galileo was delivered over to the custody of his very dear friend Ambassador Niccolini at the Villa Medici on the Pincian Hill, whose beautiful gardens had been such a joy to him on earlier, happier occasions. He spent twelve days there, very downcast about the abjuration which he

[1] Translation from John Elliot Drinkwater (— Bethune), *The Life of Galileo Galilei*, op. cit.

had not thought would be demanded of him. Then he was allowed to leave Rome, become intolerable for him, and to stay with another good friend and admirer, Ascanio Piccolomini, Archbishop of Siena. Suor Maria Celeste wrote him a rapturous letter when she heard this news: 'I wish I could describe the rejoicing of all the Mothers and Sisters on hearing of your happy arrival in Siena. It was most extraordinary. On hearing the news the Mother Abbess and many of the nuns ran to me, embracing me and weeping for joy and tenderness.' He spent five months with the archbishop, and the French poet Saint-Amant, among many other distinguished visitors, saw him 'in a room richly furnished and its walls hung with silk tapestries', busily at work with his host on the theory of mechanics.

But his heart was in Arcetri with Suor Maria Celeste, and he obtained permission from the Holy Office to return to his house and farm there, next door to the convent of his beloved. In the last days of his fatal year, 1633, the Grand Duke of Tuscany visited him at Arcetri, which gave him some hope that he might be freed from the hampering and humiliating conditions of house arrest. Alas, it was not to be. That extraordinary Pope Urban still bore him enmity and even let it be known that if he urged any more petitions for release, he would be confined in the real prison of the Inquisition.

Then a new and terrible blow fell. His darling Maria Celeste who had been worn out by anxiety over him during his trial and condemnation fell desperately ill and died on April 2, 1634, having just turned the age of thirty-three. Galileo was so broken that his life seemed in jeopardy.

'The hernia,' he wrote, 'has become more serious, and the palpitations worse. An immense sadness and melancholy, complete loss of appetite and disgust with my existence, make me feel that I am being continually called by my dearest daughter'.

In spite of everything, the amazing old man went on working at his great book on mechanics, which was to ensure his immortal fame. But again fate struck and he began to grow progressively blind. At the beginning of the year 1638, he wrote to his good Protestant friend Diodati, resident in France, 'Woe is me, signor mio, your dear friend and servant Galileo has become totally and irreparably blind'. Castelli wrote of this tragedy, 'the noblest eye is darkened which nature ever made, an eye that had seen more than the eyes of all that are gone and that had opened the eyes of all men to come'. In February of that year a petition got up by Castelli and signed by medical men was presented to the Holy Office. The reply shows well the animus of the pope who gave orders that the Florentine Inquisitor was to visit Galileo with a doctor and report on his condition. He was also to find out whether, if Galileo were permitted to return to his house in Florence for treatment, there would be any danger of his starting propaganda for his condemned opinion that the earth goes round the sun.

The Inquisitor, one Muzzarelli Fanano, reported that he was so reduced 'as to appear more like a corpse than a living man'. Permission was then graciously conceded for his return temporarily to his house in Florence, but with strict injunctions to stay indoors and not on any account raise the Copernican question, on pain of formal prison and excommunication reserved to His Holiness. The seclusion was so rigorous that a special decree had to be obtained from the pope before Galileo could go to hear Mass at a little church only a few paces distant from his house. The Dutch government awarded him a magnificent gold chain for services he had rendered them, but the Inquisition would not allow him to accept it. So the petty persecution went on.

In spite of it Galileo continued to dictate new chapters of his *Dialogues Concerning Two New Sciences*. The dynamics and statics which he had investigated eagerly in his Paduan days, twenty-five years earlier, and then abandoned to engage on his Copernican crusade, were at last brought to birth as sciences strictly so called. 'The crusade had ended in a fiasco,' wrote Arthur Koestler, 'and out of the shambles modern physics was born'. He had his son Vincenzo living with him at Arcetri and his son's charming wife to take the place of the vanished Maria Celeste. Evangelista Torricelli, a celebrated scientist in his own right, joined the little circle in 1641. Galileo's future biographer and complete devotee, Vincenzo Viviani, very young and enthusiastic, also regularly appeared. And best and dearest friend of any, the incomparable Benedetto Castelli was always there when needed. John Milton, another famous man destined to go blind, visited him in 1638.

Having at length finished his *Dialogues Concerning Two New Sciences*, Galileo was confronted with the problem of getting that masterpiece published, for he was forbidden

12. On the right is the Dun...

13. Viviani's sketch of a pendulum clock (?) made at Galileo's dictation after he became blind.

to publish anything. However, the very distinguished Dutch firm of Elzevir undertook the work and gave it to the world in a splendid volume at Leyden in July, 1638. Out of a spirit of devilment Galileo employed the same three figures Salviati, Sagredo and Simplicio in the *Dialogues* as in the *Dialogue*, but they do not engage in polemics and speak only in the objective interests of science and truth.

On November 5, 1641, the worn-out, persecuted Don Quixote of the sun and stars, broken by charging Aristotelian windmills, took to his bed, received the last sacraments of the Church to which in spite of pope and cardinals he remained ever faithful, and died with his good friends praying round his bed on January 8, 1642, at four o'clock in the morning.

Little more need be said except that the question of papal infallibility does not arise. Galileo's condemnation was an administrative action of the Congregation of the Holy Office, which the Pope neither signed nor ratified. No one has ever tried to maintain that the Holy Office is infallible. The pope was wrong and stupid in his action but he never taught officially and as supreme pastor of the Church that heliocentrism was heretical. He did not even personally think so but only that the theory was rash as things stood and unsettling to simple minds. What is most to be deplored in his conduct is the meanness and vindictiveness of his attitude to a towering genius whom he had once so warmly admired.

Brief Bibliography of Works in English

DRAKE, STILLMAN. *Discoveries and Opinions of Galileo.* (New York, 1957.) This admirable and very cheap book contains translations, with introductions and notes, of *The Starry Messenger* (1610), *Letters on Sunspots* (1613), *Letter to the Grand Duchess Christina* (1615), and, in part only, *The Assayer* (1623). Mr Drake has published also the only complete modern translation of the *Dialogue Concerning the Two Great World Systems* (Berkeley, 1953).

GEBLER, KARL VON. *Galileo Galilei and the Roman Curia.* Translated from the German. (London, 1879.) In many respects this book, by a brilliant young Protestant scholar, is still the best available in English, especially for its elaborate documentation.

KOESTLER, ARTHUR. *The Sleepwalkers.* A History of Man's changing Vision of the Universe. (London, 1959.) Mr Koestler was trained as a scientist and worked as reporter of scientific gatherings until politics claimed him. He has now happily reverted to his first love, and this book, like nearly all of his many books, makes fascinating reading. He admits to a certain bias against Galileo because of that genius's alleged shabby treatment of his hero Kepler. St Robert Bellarmine is accounted by Mr Koestler to have realized the true nature of scientific thought, as against Galileo!

SANTILLANA, GIORGIO DE. *The Crime of Galileo.* (Chicago, 1955.) This book is worth reading for its sheer verve and enthusiasm. The enthusiasm, however, leads the Professor to a good deal of confused thinking. He is quite understandably strongly anti-clerical but his portrait of St Robert Bellarmine, the chief villain of the book, is a mere caricature. The book abounds in valuable citations from the literature of the subject.

TAYLOR, SHERWOOD F. *Galileo and the Freedom of Thought.* (London, 1938.) This book was issued by Watts & Co., publishers to the Rationalist Press Association, and was meant to promote the Rationalist cause, but the writing of it brought the author into the Catholic Church. It is an admirable and most readable book, but the publishers have allowed it to go out of print and it is now extremely difficult to acquire a copy even at second hand. This is a great pity.

148

Index

Acquaviva, Claudio 115
Almagest, the 18
Aquinas, Thomas 18, 42
Archimedes 64-5
Aristotelians 17, 19, 40n., 41, 44, 61, 138
Aristotle
  physical system of the heavens 17-18;
  pre-eminence of 18-19;
  De Anima 42;
  on floating and sinking bodies 64
Assayer, The (see Saggiatore, Il)
Astronomical and Philosophical Balance, The 116
Averroes 42

Barberini, Cardinal Francesco 135
Barberini, Cardinal Maffeo 65, 91, 116, 117
  see also Urban VIII
Bellarmine, Cardinal Robert 58, 59, 62, 63, 69, 89, 92, 93, 96, 101, 104, 105, 106, 107, 108, 109, 130, 131-3, 134n.
Bessel, Friedrich 81

Boccherini, Geri 131
Borgia, Cardinal 128
Brahe, Tycho 38, 39, 50, 115

Caccini, Matteo 88
Caccini, Fra Tommaso, O.P. 86-8, 98, 115, 138
cannocchiale, see telescope
Capra, Baldassar 25
Castelli, Benedetto, O.S.B. 41, 73-4, 76, 79, 80, 85, 88, 89, 93, 96, 122, 124, 130, 143, 144
Cesi, Prince 57, 58, 85, 93, 122
Christina, Grand Duchess of Lorraine 75, 80, 117
Christmann 41
Ciampoli, Giovanni 91, 92, 93, 124
Cigoli, Ludovico Cardi da 83
Clavius, Fr Christopher, S.J. 50, 51, 52, 57, 58, 61
Colombe, Ludovico delle 52, 66
Commentary on Book of Job (Stunica) 97, 104, 106
compass, geometric and military 24
Copernicus, Nicholas 18, 50, 89, 90, 91, 115, 131, 132, 139;

149

Copernicus, Nicholas—*cont.*
  De Revolutionibus Orbium Coelestium,
    q.v.;
  planetary system of 35, 36, 39, 49
Copleston, F.C. 42n.
Cremonini, Cesare 41, 63

del Monte, Cardinal 22, 56, 62, 92
del Monte, Marchese Guido Ubaldo
    20, 22, 23, 92
De Revolutionibus Orbium Coelestium
    18, 81-3, 96, 104, 106
Dialogue on the Two Great World
    Systems 36, 114, 120-1, 123-4,
    127, 128, 129, 135, 136-7, 138
Dialogues Concerning Two New Sciences
    144-5
Dini, Mgr Piero 89, 92, 93
Discourse on the Comets 116
Discourse on Things that Float or Move
    on Water 65, 66, 74, 83
Divino Afflante Spiritu 96
Drake, Stillman 20n., 30n., 33, 34n.,
    40n., 46n., 47, 48n., 49n., 114,
    116, 134n.
Drinkwater, John Elliot 58n., 141n.

Fanano, Muzzarelli 143
Farnese, Cardinal 58
Ferdinand II de' Medici 121, 124,
    129, 142
Foscarini, Paolo Antonio 92-3, 96,
    104, 106, 131-2

Galen, Claudius 15
Galilei, Galileo
  birth and childhood 14
  and family 22, 23
  education 15-16
  professor of mathematics at Pisa
    16, 17; at Padua 20
  conflict with Aristotelians 17
  theory of falling bodies 19
  and mechanics 19-20
  health 20
  children 20-22; *see also* Maria
    Celeste; Galilei, Vincenzo
    literary lectures 22
  remunerations: at Pisa 22; at
    Padua 23; for spyglass 31;
    as mathematician to Grand
    Duke of Tuscany 46
  private lessons 24

  tutor to Cosimo II, de' Medici 24-5
  hostility to 31
  observations of moon 31
  observations of fixed stars 31-2
  observations of Jupiter 33-5
  chief mathematician and philoso-
    pher to Grand Duke of Tus-
    cany 46
  head mathematician at Univers-
    ity of Pisa 46
  observations of Saturn 48-9
  discovers phases of Venus 50-1
  wins approval of Jesuits 51
  audience with Paul V 56
  elected member of Accademia dei
    Lincei 57
  on floating and sinking of bodies
    in water 64-5
  sunspots 66-8
  views on science and religion 76-9
  knowledge of scripture and ex-
    egesis 79
  and the Preface of *De Revolutioni-*
    bus 81-3
  and Lorini 84-6
  and Caccini 86-8
  denounced to Inquisition 98
  admonished by Bellarmine 104-5
  further audience with Paul V 107
  Bellarmine's certificate 108-9
  called back to Florence 113
  theory of the tides 114
  Grassi and *Il Saggiatore* 115-7
  Urban refuses to rescind decree
    117-8
  returns to Florence 118; Suor
    Maria Celeste 118-20
  begins *Dialogue* (*q.v.*) 120
  illness 120
  completes *Dialogue* 121
  Dialogue printed 124
  summoned before the Inquisition
    129
  first interrogation 131-4
  second interrogation 135
  his confession 136-7
  third examination and sentence
    139-40
  recites formula of abjuration
    140-1
  returns to Arcetri 142
  writes *Dialogues Concerning Two*
    New Sciences 143-5

last illness and death 144-5
Publications: handbook for compass (1606) 25; *Sidereus Nuncius q.v.*; *Dialogue q.v.*; *Discourse on Floating Bodies q.v.*; *History and Demonstrations Concerning Sunspots and their Phenomena q.v.*; *Letter to Grand Duchess Christina q.v.*; *Letters on Sunspots q.v.*; *Saggiatore, Il q.v.*; *Dialogue Concerning the Two Great World Systems q.v.*
Galilei, Michelangelo 22, 43
Galilei, Vincenzo (father of Galileo) 14, 15, 22
Galilei, Vincenzo (son of Galileo) 20, 22
Galilei, Virginia (*see* Maria Celeste)
Gamba, Marina 20-22
Gebler, Karl von 62n., 107n., 134n., 137n.
Grassi, Orazio 63, 115-6, 124, 138
Grienberger, Fr, S. J. 61, 63, 89, 90
Gordian Knot, The 41
Gualdo, Paolo 68-9
Guicciardini, Piero 101, 102, 122
  letters to Picchena 101-2, 102-3
Guiducci, Mario 116

Heliocentrism 39, 50, 108-9, 121
  as hypothesis or reality 80-83
Hipparchus 18
History and Demonstrations Concerning Sunspots and their Phenomena 73
Holy Office 62, 85, 89, 101, 102, 103, 104, 105, 106, 140, 141, 142, 143, 145
Horky 44

Inquisition, the Roman 43, 48n., 66, 104, 118, 129, 130, 131, 144, 145

Jesuits 47-8, 69n.
  in China 38, 124
  astronomers, attitude to Copernicanism 40
  expulsion from Venice 43
  ordered to defend Aristotle 115
Jupiter 17, 33-5, 41, 44, 48, 59, 60-1

Kepler, Johannes 38-9, 50, 64, 114

A New Astronomy, or a Physics of the Sky (*Astronomia Nova*) 38, 40n.
Podromus 40n.
Dissertatio cum Nuncio Sidereo 44
Koestler, Arthur 35-8n., 39, 40n., 114, 144

Leo XIII 97
Leopold, Archduke 114
Letter to Grand Duchess Christina 80, 97
Letters on Sunspots 84, 104, 115
Libri, Giulio 51
Lincei, Accademia dei 57-8, 67, 68
Lipperhey, Hans 30
Lorini, Niccolò 84-6, 88, 89
Luther, Martin 39, 82

Maculano da Firenzuola, Fra Vincenzo 131-3, 135
Magini 44, 50
Maraffi, Fra Luigi, O.P. 87
Maria Celeste, Suor (Virginia Galilei) 20, 21, 118-20, 122-3, 134-5, 142, 144
Mars 17, 38-9
Marzimedici, Archbishop of Florence 83
Medicean planets 44, 45, 56
Medicean stars 30, 41
Medici, Cosimo II 24, 44, 56, 73, 117
Melanchthon 82
Mercury 17
Milky Way 33
Milton, John 144
Moon, the 17, 50, 59, 60
  Galileo's observation of (1609) 31-2

Newton, Isaac 39, 114
Niccolini, Caterina 123, 129
Niccolini, Francesco 121, 123, 124, 130, 141

Olney, Mary Allan 79, 118, 123n.
Orion 32, 33
Orsini, Cardinal 103
Osiander 82, 96

Padua, University of 20, 23, 41
Pandolfini 84-5
Parallax 80-81

Paul III, Pope 18, 66
Paul V, Pope 43, 56-7, 104
Pendulum 16
Pereira, Benedict, S.J. 79, 96
Picchena, Curzio 101, 102, 107
Piccolomini, Ascanio, Archbishop of Siena 142
Pinelli, Giovanni Vincenzo 23
Pisa 13f.
  University of 15-16
  Cathedral of 13, 16
  Galileo, head mathematician at 46
Pius XII, Pope 96
planetary motion, early Greek theory of 17, 18
  Galileo's observations of 33-5
  Tycho Brahe's theory of 37, 39
Pleiades, the 32, 33
Providentissimus Deus 97
Ptolemy 18, 50, 91, 139

Riccardi, Niccolò, O.P. 121-2, 124, 127

Saggiatore, Il (The Assayer) 63, 115-7, 120
Sagredo, Giovanni Francesco 23, 46, 47, 107, 121, 145
Salviati, Filippo 49n., 83, 121, 145
Santillana, Giorgio de 69n., 115, 124, 138
Sarpi, Paolo 23, 43
Saturn 17, 48-9
Scheiner, Fr Christopher, S.J. 48n., 67-8, 76, 124
Sfondrati, Cardinal 85, 89

Sidereus Nuncius, 29, 34, 38, 40, 44, 67, 97
Siger de Brabant 42
Sizi, Francesco 55-6
spy-glass, *see* telescope
Starry Messenger, The, see Sidereus Nuncius
stars, fixed 17, 32, 34, 59, 60, 61
Stunica, Didacus à 97, 104, 106
Sun, the 17
  see heliocentrism, sunspots
sunspots 66-8, 137

telescope 17, 30, 31, 35-8n., 42, 48
tides, theory of the 114, 121, 137
Torricelli, Evangelista 144
Trent, Council of 94, 96

Urban VIII, Pope 117, 119, 121, 123, 127, 128, 130, 137-8, 139 (and note) 145. *see also* Barberini, Cardinal Maffeo

Venice, Republic of 20, 21, 42
  Doge and Council of 31, 43, 46
  Government and City under interdict 43
Venus 17, 49, 50, 59, 60, 62
Vinta, Belisario 44, 56
Viviani, Vincenzo 83, 144

Welser, Mark 49n., 50, 67
Wohlwill, Emil 106

Zuñiga, Diego de, *see* Stunica, Didacus à